Josiah Royce's Seminar, 1913–1914

Dec. 9, 1913.]

R: As the props. "There are values" a primitive prop.

Bergson: In ethical systems, yes.

Discussion about ethical systems, Bentham.

Royce: Is prop. above from self-evidence, or a dogma, or a postulate

Bergson: Postulate, but a needed postulate.

[nature & function of definition. Russell, K. Schmidt

are they equations expressing a contention.]

T.S. Eliot. Primitive religions.

Problems: On comparative religion, in how far is

it description & in how far interpretation.

Can you treat religion as a form of social behavior &

what is behavior (the Primitive mind's interpretation

of its behavior is part of its behavior & interpretation

of an early behavior)

Based on Durkheim: Règles d. l. méthode sociol.

Representation collective etc. (Rev de Mét)

Lévy-Bruhl – Fonctions mentale dans les sociétés

On Max Müller scientific definition is forcing

confused with philosophic interpretation, same

in recent times. Can any sci. religion be arrived at.

Protest against evolution of religion. No standard

of evolution.

JOSIAH ROYCE'S SEMINAR, 1913-1914:
as recorded in the notebooks
of HARRY T. COSTELLO

Edited by GROVER SMITH
With an Essay on the Philosophy of Royce
by Richard Hocking

Rutgers University Press   New Brunswick   New Jersey

ᏏᏙ PREFACE

Harry Todd Costello used two secretarial notebooks in recording Josiah Royce's seminar, at Harvard, in 1913–14. They are now in the Library of Trinity College, Hartford. The two are alike, measuring about eight and three-eighths by five and three-eighths inches, with marbled-paper board covers hinged at the top and labeled "Harvard Coöperative Society." On the label of the first he wrote: "H. T. Costello, 26 Irving Street. Royce: Seminary in Comparative Methodology, 1913–1914." On the label of the second he modified this legend, substituting the title "Seminary on Scientific Methods." He entered his notes in longhand on the rectos of the leaves from front to back and on the versos from back to front, in this way completing the first notebook but, in the second, breaking off shortly after changing direction. Two leaves are missing from the first without interruption of continuity. The pencilled notes on each meeting except the opening meeting of the year are immediately followed by a summary, in ink, designed to be read aloud in the seminar. The summaries are easily legible; the notes, however, besides being in a more rapid hand, present difficulties in the form of interlinings, unsystematic punctuation, vague abbreviations (e.g., "mech." for "mechanism," "mechanistic," or "mechanical"; "psych." for "psychology," "psychologist," or "psychological"), and the like. In transcribing the contents of the notebooks, the editor has worked mainly from positive photostats, but has scrutinized the originals in an attempt, fortunately with good results, to fix on true readings in several dozen doubtful passages. He has also had the advantage to his eyesight of consulting at various stages a rough typescript copy thoughtfully provided by the publisher.

The editor has expanded abbreviations and, for the most part in the notes, has modified the capitalization, punctuation, and paragraphing wherever the sense was unambiguous yet would not be readily grasped. He has tried to keep such changes to a minimum. He has silently normalized the spelling, as of proper names, has corrected minor redundancies and syntactical slips, and has repaired inaccuracies in the citation of page numbers from books and articles. Titles that are abridged in the manuscript he has restored; the titles here printed in brackets he has supplied, the reference in each case of this sort being definite, unless otherwise indicated, and useful in clarifying the context. Other bracketed matter he has inserted either after collating the notes with the summaries or after comparing the digests of papers with ascertainable sources of the subject-matter or, when available, with printed versions. He is solely responsible for the footnotes and of course for the index of names. He has omitted nothing of substance found in the manuscript except certain illustrative diagrams, a few marginal notations, and, regretfully, a gallery of abstract designs and of grotesque faces bearing a tribal likeness to Palmer Cox's troops of brownies.

Hitherto unpublished material from the Peirce papers in the Houghton Library, relating to the correspondence between Charles S. Peirce and Frederick A. Woods, is cited or quoted here by permission of the Department of Philosophy of Harvard University. Costello's "Recollections of Royce's Seminar on Comparative Methodology" is reprinted, as Appendix A, by permission of the directors of the *Journal of Philosophy*. The check list of Costello's published writings, Appendix B, has been compiled by the editor with the assistance of Bryan Gillespie.

The editor wishes to acknowledge the rich and generous help of those former students of Josiah Royce who have furnished information, given leave to quote from their letters, or shown the means of solving textual problems. For blunders and misunderstandings he takes full blame, but for whatever insight into the nature—the greatness—of Royce's seminar he may have exhibited through his efforts in the following pages, he thanks Albert P. Brogan, Frances Rousmaniere Dewing, Marion Coats Graves, Leal A. Headley, Victor F. Lenzen, Jacob Loewenberg, and Florence Webster. Indeed a number of people, by responding to inquiries or by figuratively opening doors, have helped make this edition possible or in some way have affected its character. The editor desires to recognize the diverse contributions of Kenneth W. Cameron, Romane L. Clark, Marian Clarke, Carolyn Eisele, Kimball C. Elkins, Donald B. Engley, Roderick Firth, Max H. Fisch, Clarence I. Lewis, Rev. Frank M. Oppenheim, S.J., Robert L. M. Underhill, and George I. Van Riper, and, with especial gratitude, those of William Sloane, of Helen Stewart, and of Mary M. Meehan, the secretary of the Harvard University Archives. He records also his appreciation of a fellowship and of funds for travel granted by the Duke University Council on Research.

To Houston Peterson and Odell Shepard, for their indispensable reminiscences in conversation, and to Jacob Loewenberg, he would offer his share in this work of their friend Harry Costello.

GROVER SMITH

Durham, North Carolina
November, 1962

৯ CONTENTS

⮞ PROCESS AND ANALYSIS IN
THE PHILOSOPHY OF ROYCE

I. *"New Processes of Social Aggregation"*

Portraits of Royce show a person with a serene brow more than usually broad, and with a level, steady gaze. The notebooks of Professor Costello give us the same person in the community of his "Seminary in Logic," acting as the sustainer of dialogue, probing with questions, maintaining perspective.

The composition of the seminar was unusual, for it included in addition to the regularly enrolled graduate students a number of professional colleagues, representing a variety of sciences, in more or less regular attendance. Their partnership with Royce made the year's consideration of scientific methods pre-eminently cogent. After Royce's death a grateful university recorded, "His most notable contribution to the teaching of the university was made through his seminary in logic, which became a veritable clearinghouse of science. Men of widely different training and technique—chemists, physiologists, statisticians, pathologists, mathematicians—who could not understand one another, were here interpreted to one another by Royce, who understood them all." * Where else in the world at that time was such a community of scholars to be found?

* "Josiah Royce," *Science*, N.S. XLIV (December 1, 1916), 773. See J. H. Cotton, *Royce on the Human Self* (Cambridge, Massachusetts, 1954), p. 12.

Not only was the seminar remarkable over the years in its membership, but the particular year 1913–1914, for which we have the notebooks, was an important one in the history of the seminar in that it records so clearly Royce's loyalty to his gifted friend, Charles Peirce. At the session of April 28 the death of Peirce called forth a tribute from Royce which was the unplanned climax of an appreciation running through the year's work. Letters from Peirce had been read and discussed in earlier sessions of the seminar. And Royce's lecture on "The Mechanical, the Historical, and the Statistical," shared with the seminar on March 3, was focused on Peirce's ingenious statistical theory of cosmic evolution.

This lecture on "The Mechanical, the Historical, and the Statistical" gives us an important clue to understanding both the significance of the participation of scientific colleagues and the expressed indebtedness of the group and its leader to Peirce. The lecture had been prepared in the first instance for a group of colleagues invited to meet in Royce's house. It is in effect an invitation, indeed an appeal, to these colleagues to form a community of interpretation for the discussion of "questions of common scientific interest." Royce was convinced that such a community was the best laboratory for achieving new insights. It would illustrate socially the principle of "the fecundity of aggregation" which can be demonstrated in the statistical operations of Nature itself. "Do you wish to experiment upon some new processes of social aggregation?" says Royce to his friends, putting the question deliberately into the context of Peirce's evolutionary doctrine as he had come to subscribe to it.

Two years later Royce died. But his community of scientists and philosophers persisted. In the course of events certain members of it were decisive agents in bringing Whitehead to this country to continue what Peirce and Royce had begun as cosmological thinkers with mathematical leanings.* Royce, through his seminar and its associated group of scientific colleagues, appears as the mid-

* W. E. Hocking, "Whitehead As I Knew Him," *Journal of Philosophy*, LVIII (September 14, 1961), 507–08.

dle term between Peirce and Whitehead in the rise of philosophical cosmology in this country.

As we read the notebooks of 1913–1914, so faithfully kept by Professor Costello, it is well to bear in mind that by that time all of Royce's major books had already been published. His first publication was a booklet, the *Primer of Logical Analysis*, prepared by Royce as a young instructor in English at Berkeley in 1881. The *Primer*, as a work in "analysis," even though it is elementary, is in direct line of continuity with the seminar of 1913–1914. The *Primer*'s three successors, all appearing in the 'eighties, were respectively a work in metaphysics, a historical treatise, and a novel. Fortunately for philosophy in this country, the logical and metaphysical works anticipated the persistent lines of his mental growth. The historian in Royce did persist in the form of intellectual historian with special emphasis on modern philosophy. (Indeed, his Harvard title during most of his teaching years was "Professor of the History of Philosophy.") But the systematic thinker won out.

II. Three Characteristic Themes

Royce's thought was strongly influenced by the critical philosophy of Kant as well as by the post-Kantian philosophy of will in its development by Fichte and Schopenhauer. He was also well aware of the new mathematics and mathematical logic of his time. Furthermore, like most of his contemporaries in philosophy he was preoccupied with issues raised by the Darwinian theory of evolution, especially those concerning human destiny. In the course of working out his own resolution of philosophical problems he came to refer to his position as Absolute Pragmatism, meaning by this a pragmatism with some rational and moral constants in it. "Truth meets needs: truth is also true." He expressed thus his conviction that human existence is at once thoroughly time-immersed as a sequence of practical actions and, in its rational power, capable of grasping forms of order and lawfulness which are true throughout the relativities of the temporal flux. Royce is a kind of process philosopher.

a. The Postulational Logic of the Will: The Kantian and post-Kantian bent of Royce's thought is evident in the central role that he assigns to the rational activity of "postulation." His emphasis on necessary postulates of reason has about it the quality of Kant's necessary postulates of morality. In the Kantian philosophy, if it were not for the three great postulates concerning human persons and the Divine Judge, any constructive metaphysics would be largely forfeit and we would be left with a theory of knowledge for the most part negative in its critical character. The Kantian type of approach to metaphysics through the primacy of practical reason is reflected in Royce's postulational logic of the will.

A central illustration will support this point. Having in mind that Royce's metaphysics is person-centered, we are not surprised that he finds the clue to cosmic order in those principles which generate a community of moral individuals. It follows that Royce must give particular attention to the nature of individuality and to "the principle of individuation." He does so in terms of the thesis that personal individuality is a matter of "postulation." A person's individuality is not a "given" item of experience in each passing moment of his life. His uniqueness has to be affirmed by a decision of will carried through the sequence of actions which is his life. Individuality is a resolve. Likewise the individuality of others whom one encounters is decisional. Each person affirms rather than observes the uniqueness of another person as the hidden clue to the coherences of his seen courses of action.

A second illustration, closely linked with the first, is Royce's account of the structure of time. Since a life is a series of deeds in the flow of time, and since only the passing moment is at hand in experience as a decidedly cramped space of actuality, the past and the future of each person's life are constantly postulated by him in rationally deliberate remembering and anticipating. There is something here of the Augustinian insight into the connection between time's tripartite form and a triad of conscious human acts. Past, present, and future are functions of remembering, perceiving, and anticipating.

Postulations are not free and whimsical acts but free and necessary ones. The test of their necessity lies in the attempt to affirm the negative, and the logical discovery that in trying to do so the positive is inescapably reaffirmed. For example, to reject the postulate of one's individuality is to reinstate it in the very act which generates the denial, for one's individuality resides in the act itself.

These illustrations are in the spirit of Royce's view that the logic of the will is the ground of all logic. From his pragmatic conviction that all ideas are "plans of action," it plainly follows that thinking itself is a clarified aspect of willing.

b. The New Mathematics and the Logic of Yes and No: Royce liked to trace this will-centered logic to its root in "the logic of yes and no," the logic of decision and of the rational consequences of decision. The distinction between intentional affirmation and denial he called "the earliest exact relation defined by the human mind." He was confident that the new algebra of logic, and most or all of the new mathematical analyses of serial order, could be shown to be implicit in this familiar and inescapably human beginning.

The intentional acts expressed by "Yes" and "No" are personal and free, but mathematical-logical order is objective in its necessity; and yet the freedom and the objectivity go together. Royce insists that in this exact domain creating *is* discovering. By intellectual construction of numbers, or propositions, a finite thinker both launches and explores forms of serial order. The world which confronts the finite thinker is the intellectual prolongation of these series *ad infinitum*. It picks up where the finite thinker leaves off, with the same rationale; its rational constitution extrapolates from these beginnings. Thus the human intellectual creator discovers progressively the full import of what was latent in his freedom. Man "serializes" in a world which is through and through intelligibly serial. Royce's pragmatic activism of ideas, both mathematical and logical, is inseparable from a realism of these same intelligible structures. They are disclosed in ventures of intellectual freedom as necessarily the way they are.

Royce's reliance on the free rational activity of "constructing" or "creating" in mathematics and logic is quite evidently in keeping with Kant's view that mathematical thought is based on rule-guided construction of the ordered entities thought about. Royce is, in this respect, akin to mathematicians known today as "intuitionists," for example H. Poincaré, of whom he wrote with appreciation. But a major departure from Kantian doctrine comes to light here. In his judgment, neither mathematical nor logical creation is grounded in any such principle of sensory necessity as Kant proposes in his "transcendental aesthetic." The receptive "sensings" of space and time upon which Kant is insistent have nothing in common with Royce's rational activism, where the genesis of types of rational order is concerned. For Royce, the necessary milieu of such order is activity (willing), not passivity (sensing). Rational and creative will is the principle for mathematics and logic alike; wherefore the distinction between the two disciplines is canceled, and the two are regarded as branches of a single system.

Royce thus subscribes unreservedly to the impressive extension of the "algebraic" treatment of mathematical and logical problems which was taking place during his lifetime. This is apparent in his earliest book, the *Primer of Logical Analysis,* with its tribute to Boole. It is still evident in one of his latest essays, "An Extension of the Algebra of Logic," in which he explores a difficulty in Boolean algebra. The difficulty is one he found pointed out by Whitehead. It has to do with the inability of Boolean algebra to avail itself of the full power of "group operations" such as give "progressive" character to other algebras.

This adherence to the algebraic merging of mathematics and logic on the pragmatic basis of "the logic of yes and no" permits Royce to claim that a new form of "deduction of the categories" is in the making. The common principles disclosed in the new theory of order, in terms of classes, relations, and series, are in effect a

"deduced," that is, necessary, categorial scheme meeting the re-
quirements of the Kantian deduction of the categories. He regards
these common principles as final replacements of the Kantian
scheme since they possess the clarity, exactitude, and economy of
modern analysis.

c. "The World Is a Progressively Realized Community of Interpretation": These words may be read above an entrance to Royce
Hall on the Los Angeles campus of the University of California.
They give the thesis of Royce's cosmology in its mature expression.
In fact this assertion is the outcome of the argument in Volume II
of *The Problem of Christianity*, which appeared in print earlier in
the very year in which Professor Costello began his notebooks. Here
is essentially Royce's counter to Darwinian theory. He is affirming a
teleology of evolution in which the world's progress has meaning
through fostering the life of persons in community under an ethics
of loyalty.

The term "interpretation" refers to an activity which is at once
social and logical, an activity which tends to be normative in the
relations of human community. Its nature is to generate a temporal
series of deeds. A person in the present moment mediates between
one who is earlier and one who is to come, so that past signs of meaning are clarified and conserved into the future. The social molecule
is a three-membered group composed of a person who gives a sign of
meaning which calls for interpretation, a person who interprets,
and a person who receives the interpretation. The serial nature of
such triadic relations evidently harmonizes with Royce's conception of a serial and progressive logic of the will. The mathematical
analysis of types of serial order permits the analysis in exact terms
of the rational anatomy of this social process.

But Royce does not stop here. When he speaks of the "world" as
a community of interpretation, he is taking the daring step of judging the social categories of human existence to be the clue to natural
order as well. This is more than a reaffirmation of one of his earliest
convictions (from 1880 and before) that this is "a world of life."
With encouragement from the researches of his friend Charles

xviii JOSIAH ROYCE'S SEMINAR

Peirce, he is holding the view that Nature is constitutionally fitted to enter into the most rational type of human interpretation, namely that of the community of scientists. In "science," the nonhuman things of Nature spontaneously give signs of meaning to man, their interpreter, whose interpretations are received and weighed ("verified") by future things of Nature. Nature seems to be predisposed to scientific interpretation and to have evolved its proper interpreter in the shape of scientific mankind. The success of modern pragmatic natural science is weighty evidence for this hypothesis. This reflection invites the inference that the natural world and mankind differ in degree only, and belong together in a larger community of conscious entities as extensive as the universe.

Royce tentatively explores the implications of this "Universal Sociology" with the help of his theory of time. His hypothesis is "that we have no right whatever to speak of really unconscious Nature, but only of uncommunicative Nature, or of Nature whose mental processes go on at such different time-rates from ours that we cannot adjust ourselves to a live appreciation of their inward fluency. . . ." * In a world process in which many threads of life, human and nonhuman, are interweaving, the interpretive activity goes on throughout many grades of less and more comprehensive time relations and less and more coherent logical relations. Just as infrapersonal life sustains its ordered progress by way of its more and more comprehensive interpreter, scientific mankind, so, Royce proposes in a great analogy, infrapersonal and personal lives sustain their joint ordered progress by way of their nonfinite and altogether comprehensive interpreter, *The* Interpreter, whose continuing action is "the Spirit of the World's Infinite Community." The necessities inherent in the world's serial order are at once the character of the Infinite Will which sustains and conserves the progress of all finite conscious beings. Here we have in new formulation an *itinerarium mentis in deum* for all that lives, namely for all beings. Royce's social metaphysics is a theology.

* *The World and the Individual* (New York, 1901), II, 225–26.

Having in mind three such general themes characteristic of Royce's thought, the reader of the notebooks should be in a position to recognize, in the wide range of topics which were discussed in the seminar of 1913–1914, suggestions of a coherent guiding interest. The mathematical side of Royce's interest, for instance, is evident in the several discussions of statistics and probability. The concern with a philosophy of evolution can be seen in such topics as the fitness of the environment and the contrast of mechanics and history. The voluntaristic view of science itself invites the discussions of value and interpretation.

III. *Why the Neglect, and Why the Renewal of Interest?*

During the years between the two world wars the more active philosophical interests in North America led away from a teleological type of metaphysics such as that of Royce. His thought underwent eclipse for a generation. Since the Second World War, partly with a stimulus from France, a careful study of Royce's philosophy has been resumed. A glance at some of the reasons for this change of fortune will help to a clearer understanding of Royce's thought.

When we recall the complex alignments in philosophy during the 'twenties and 'thirties, particularly in this country, we are hard put to it to discern a general issue beneath the surface of the many special issues. One possibility is the metaphysical issue of teleology. Note, for example, that various forms of pragmatism were congenial to teleology in evolutionary form. And Royce's type of pragmatic idealism was more explicitly teleological than most.

a. Teleology Analyzed Away: The schools of realism of the American and English varieties tended to discourage teleological doctrines. Generally speaking, "realism" represented a focus of attention on the theory of knowledge in detachment from metaphysical problems, or at least with neutrality toward a wide range of metaphysical issues. To the extent that such realistic movements made their influence felt in American philosophy in the last generation, they drew attention away from such teleological thought as that of Royce.

Ironically, the teleological trait in Royce's philosophy which brought it into conflict with the Anglo-American realisms constituted its bond with Continental forms of realism, in particular, Scholastic philosophy, which was being renewed in his generation, and Existentialism which has become prominent in more recent years. The reader of Royce's work can hardly fail to see evidence of a wide understanding of Scholasticism on his part, and may conclude that it was the teleological character of Scholastic philosophy which made this type of realism congenial to his mind in ways in which the nonteleological realisms were not.

As the logical positivism of the Vienna Circle was transplanted to this country in the 'thirties, there grew up a movement of more sweeping repudiation of metaphysics. Not only the teleological tendency of some schools of thought, but metaphysics as such was subjected to analysis in a way which tended toward the suppression of the whole discipline. Although this movement, in some contrast to the more recent English school of language analysis, was indebted to a considerable extent to the Kantian critical tradition, it emphasized the philosophy of science contained in this tradition rather than the ethics with its metaphysical weight. Positivism, more forcefully than realism, contributed to the temporary neglect of Royce's thought.

b. American Philosophers Begin to Write Their Own History: American philosophy has been typically more concerned with systematic and speculative work than with the interpretation of intellectual history. Nevertheless, recent years have seen a vigorous increase in historical studies of American thought. These histories have, of course, identified a "classical" stage of American philosophy around the turn of the century, with William James as the central enlivener of mental combat. Inevitably, Royce and Santayana have been included in the account; and Peirce has received a delayed recognition. The renewal of attention to Royce has thus been in part a result of the historian's obligation to preserve continuity and proportion in his work of interpretation.

Curiously enough, the representatives of the more positivistic forms of philosophy have been inhibited from undertaking this historian's task. It is likely that the hermeneutic sympathy required for the writing of adequate intellectual history cannot be generated within the positivist's categorial scheme.

c. The Renewal of Cosmology: Metaphysics has grown decidedly more inductive in its procedure during the past half century, continuing the tendency begun by the nineteenth-century dialectical philosophies. The radical empiricism of William James and the phenomenology of Edmund Husserl have given programmatic expression to this development of a "wider empiricism." One outcome of this inductive emphasis has been the renewal of cosmology as a philosophical discipline, witness the achievements of Henri Bergson and Nicolai Hartmann.

The work of Peirce as a cosmologist has supported the tendency to inductive procedures in metaphysics. In addition, Whitehead's influence, especially through the writings of his American years, has strengthened this tendency. In contrast to the European philosophers Bergson and Hartmann, both Peirce and Whitehead brought their masteries of mathematics to bear directly and constructively upon their cosmological thinking, thereby giving to this branch of American philosophy a characteristically exact expression. This tendency in the newer cosmology has resulted in a renewed interest in Royce's cosmology because of its mathematical as well as its inductive character.

d. Optimistic Existentialism: When Marcel writes that Royce's philosophy "marks a transition between absolute idealism and existentialist thought," what has he in mind? The prevailing notion of Existentialism is that it is a gloomy philosophy appropriate to these gloomy times. Royce's philosophy, on the other hand, is sometimes judged too optimistic for a mid-twentieth-century taste. In the face of this discrepancy the Catholic existentialist thinker wel-

comes, in Royce, an approach to a "metaphysics of joy" which is
nonetheless pertinent to Existentialism. Marcel thus disturbs our
preconception of the existential as a synonym for the morbid. In
Royce's version of *homo viator*, as a serial order of deeds (not a
substantial monad), as concretely individual in the flux of time and
yet transcending the passing moments in the "Beloved Community," Marcel finds the American counterpart of theistic forms of
Existentialism such as have come to expression in Europe. Royce's
sense of the immanence of human in Divine creativity, especially as
clarified and completed in the "concrete a priori" of W. E. Hocking,
is virtually that *présence* which Marcel's own inductive metaphysics has so richly disclosed. The stimulus from overseas of this optimistic form of existentialist philosophy has contributed its share to
the awakened interest in Royce's thought.

IV. *Pertinence to the Present Situation:*

There are mutations occurring in the philosophical situation today to which one or another aspect of Royce's thought will contribute. Consider three tendencies selected from the complex of current
discussion which have a growing momentum.

a. The "Analytic Philosophy" is becoming noticeably more hos-
pitable to metaphysics, especially to metaphyics of an inductive
sort (despite Professor Feigl's fear of "disreputable" alliances between science and philosophy on such a basis). The temper of the
Aristotelian kind of "analytics" which pervades the British analysis
of language is a helping factor in bringing about this change. It is
to be expected that Royce's contributions to analysis, with their
pragmatic character, will gradually find their place. This is especially likely to happen as attention continues to be given to the
time-honored task of disclosing the categorial structure of things.

b. It is nearly axiomatic that the Western philosophic community will continue to widen its borders, becoming more open to the

influence of the other great intellectual traditions in the world. The "East-West" philosophical exchanges between Asian and Occidental philosophers at Honolulu and elsewhere are still at an early stage of their potential growth. Royce's philosophy has much still to contribute to this new catholicity of mind. One insight of his, based partly on his own studies of the schools of the Vedanta, is the recognition of the mystic and the realist as dialectical companions, each requiring the other. From this insight come a number of implications for the meeting of East and West.

c. The existential thinkers have so far given a more adequate phenomenology of persons in their solitude than of persons in community. Their gift has been to trace the inner history of "life's way." Since Royce's near-existential philosophy is altogether interpersonal and communal in character, his metaphysics of the "Social Infinite" (as Professor John Smith aptly calls it) will continue to add to the development of existential doctrines of man where they still fall short.

Such considerations as these of Royce's pertinence to the emerging situation do but remind us that in philosophical discourse every thinker is a contemporary and every major thinker is rightfully to be heard in the dialogue from time to time.

RICHARD HOCKING

Emory University
Atlanta, Georgia
September, 1962

ঌ EDITOR'S INTRODUCTION

In September, 1913, when Costello became for the year the "recording secretary" of Philosophy 20c and began taking notes on its weekly meetings, precisely a quarter of a century had passed since Royce first conducted his famous seminar. Over that period it had undergone various metamorphoses. Initially, in 1888–89, Royce dealt with Kant. Throughout most of the 'nineties he concentrated on the system of Hegel, returning to it from 1906 to 1908. During 1896–97, in a temporary exchange of places with William James, he explored the methods of psychology. His regular Metaphysical Seminary, as it was called, acquired officially a new name in 1903, the Logical Seminary, afterwards the Seminary in Logic; and as early as 1898 its topic was announced as the problems of logic. But it was never narrowly circumscribed by any subject. First and last it was a seminar in the contents of Royce's own versatile and capacious mind, which commanded a scale of subject matter ranging from mathematics to epistemology and from biology to ethics. Such later catalogue descriptions as "The Logical Analysis of Fundamental Concepts and their General Relations to Philosophical Problems" (1904–1906), "A Comparative Study of those Concepts of Human Thought which have to do with the Relations of Whole and Part" (1908–09), and, in the final years of Royce's life, "A Comparative Study of Various Types of Scientific Method" (1910–1912, 1913–1916) show the typical catholicity of his interests.

To Royce, human knowledge composed a unity, even if the precise form of that unity could not be crystallized. All the arts pertaining to humanity had a common bond. That was the concern of philosophy; it must also be the ultimate concern of science, as a branch of philosophy. And science increasingly fascinated him. This evolution was owing in great part to his admiration for Charles S. Peirce, who had been rejected by Harvard only to become a chief cornerstone. Royce enlisted for his seminar the aid of colleagues from many disciplines, especially the sciences. As his guests they could come to its meetings to read their newest papers and to debate with one another and with him the philosophical principles of their work. Like him, they were seeking terms of unity. Thus, one year, according to Marion Coats Graves, "We had formulated a definite problem: 'Do all pieces of research employ the same methods, so that we may properly speak of *the* scientific method as applicable to all fields of research; or do the methods vary with the fields?' Mr. Royce invited several authorities to describe to the class the method each guest used; and after discussion, we noted whether any different methods had been employed." G. A. Reisner reported on Egyptian archaeology, F. W. Taussig on the economics of the steel industry, W. B. Cannon on physiology, R. C. Cabot on ethics, and Ella Lyman Cabot on the fine arts. Victor F. Lenzen, the secretary during the final year of the seminar, as Costello had been two years earlier, has preserved in one of his own notebooks a full account of the guest papers of 1915–16. These included one by R. F. A. Hoernlé on implication and one by E. E. Southard on the logic of pathology. Royce would emphasize the unity of theme inherent in a common attention to method or logic; but, recalling 1913–14, Florence Webster testifies that this often yielded in interest to the subjects of the papers themselves. Perhaps one may conclude that the most evident unity was a psychological one, an intellectual excitement generated among the students by the almost fierce vitality of Royce.

No one long subjected to Royce's influence could underrate his thoroughness and alertness. With Costello's "Recollections of Royce's Seminar on Comparative Methodology" (1955), here reproduced as Appendix A, may be compared the reminiscences of

Jacob Loewenberg published in the *Harvard Alumni Bulletin* of January 29, 1949, where Loewenberg said:

> I can still see Royce, sitting at the head of the table in Emerson Hall (Room C), a large notebook in front of him, in which he would record minutely the visitor's discourse and his replies to questions. It was a thrilling experience to watch the encounter of critical minds and to participate in a free trade of ideas. The trade was indeed a flourishing one, for Royce appropriated from the many scholars valuable material for interpretation and synthesis, and the scholars in their turn learned to appreciate the importance and relevance of philosophy. Some of them would return to the seminar year after year. And as for the students, the vistas gained into unsuspected worlds of knowledge loosened their dogmatism and deepened their understanding.

Loewenberg, who attended the seminar at intervals from 1907–08 to 1911–12, hints further at the personal dynamism of Royce: a discussion, he observes, would consist in "an amicable altercation between Royce and his guests." The key word is "amicable"; the helpfulness of a discussion may depend on a certain intensity. Royce's searching honesty, allied to his pepperiness, animated his treatment of students. Frances Rousmaniere Dewing, with a perspective stretching now more than six decades (she was present almost every year from 1900–01 to 1905–06), sights what must have been the functional virtue of Royce's pedagogy: "He was . . . a master at perceiving and developing, sometimes by questions, germs of real interest in a paper that sounded, as it was read, confused and almost meaningless. In the conduct of the seminar, however, he made every effort to have a live discussion among the members of the group." She adds: "I want to emphasize that I found the Royce seminars really different from others I attended . . . in being *discussions*. Royce gave us the definite feeling he had respect for each speaker, and would weigh remarks thoughtfully."

Small wonder that his best students, if still in Cambridge after finishing dissertations at Harvard or Radcliffe, should have welcomed an invitation to come back as visitors.

Of course the students were expected to do more than listen and discuss. As the Costello notebooks abundantly show, nearly everybody had to join in by reading papers. Although student papers might often bear on the unifying subject of the year, in practice many of them went afield in method as well as content. They might stem from research not done expressly for the seminar, as, for instance, into materials for dissertations in progress. Royce seems to have been accustomed to speak of the papers as "notes," but Costello's terminology in his account shows that a distinction was felt between the short "note" and the long "paper," even when the latter was not written out in full. As Loewenberg has indicated, Royce would ordinarily draft, on the spot, a memorandum about each contribution. The Harvard Archives possess four battered manuscript notebooks containing such records, which cover 1901–02, 1904–05, 1909–10 (with one page on a 1907 session), and 1911–12. Some of the note-taking in 1911–12 was done by others; Royce suffered an apoplectic seizure in the middle of the year. In 1909–10 the unifying subject was "causation," which was assigned as the topic of an exercise. Both then and in 1911–12 Royce would ask one or another of the members each week to draw up a summary of the meeting and to read it the week following. He was keenly interested in the results, which he would evaluate in the privacy of his notebook.

It appears likely that 1913–14 was the first year in which Royce delegated to only one person the regular job of note-taking and summarizing; and he was to do so but once again, in 1915–16. His nomination of Costello, then an Instructor in Philosophy, must have been influenced by the quality of similar work Costello had now and then done as a student. In his notebook for 1909–10 he had twice used the characteristic phrase "very pretty," in commenting on Costello's reports.

Costello was in his twenty-eighth year, having been born on No-

vember 1, 1885, in Richmond, Indiana. He had matriculated at
Earlham College, where his first teacher of philosophy was Edwin
Diller Starbuck. After being graduated in 1908, he had come to
Harvard on a University Scholarship, had received the A.M. in
1910, and had remained to complete the doctorate the next year
while holding the James Walker Fellowship. He studied symbolic
logic under Royce and, in both 1909–10 and 1910–11, was a registered student in Philosophy 20c. In the former year he offered
seven "notes"—one on causation with respect to economic evolution, one on individuality, one on the question whether the present
fact of consciousness proves any truth beyond itself, one on psycho-
physical causation (in which he opposed "dualism"), one on an
economic example of value causation, one on Lamprecht and the
concept of history, and one on Veblen's *The Theory of Business
Enterprise*. His doctoral dissertation, accepted by a committee con-
sisting of R. B. Perry, Royce, and E. B. Holt, reflected among other
things his passion for economics. Its subject was "The Fundamental
Characteristics of Organizations, Especially as Illustrated by Those
Organizations through Which the Results of Science are Applied
to the Arts and Industries"—a pompous title which Costello may
have thought rather droll.

Obtaining a Sheldon Fellowship, he attended Bergson's lectures
at the Sorbonne in 1911–12. On his return to Harvard he became
an Assistant in Philosophy; for 1913–14 he was promoted to Instructor. During the spring of 1914 he served as Assistant Lecturer
in the advanced logic course given by Bertrand Russell. Two of
Royce's students in the 1913–14 seminar, A. P. Brogan and N. N.
Sen Gupta, were enrolled in that course, along with Raphael
Demos, E. W. Friend, C. E. Kellogg, V. F. Lenzen, and Robert L.
M. Underhill. Others, such as T. S. Eliot (then the president of the
Philosophy Club), may have "audited"; and according to Lenzen
practically everyone, including Perry, crowded into Russell's lec-
tures on theory of knowledge.

Costello left Harvard in 1914. After occupying a post at Yale for
a year, he took an Instructorship at Barnard College and then, from

1918 to 1920, a Lectureship at Columbia. During his final year in New York he did part-time teaching at the City College. In 1920 he was appointed to the chair of Brownell Professor of Philosophy at Trinity College, Hartford. Except for visiting lectureships at the University of California (1922) and Harvard (1930) and his Woodbridge Lectureship at Columbia (1952), he remained at Trinity for the rest of his career. His Woodbridge Lectures were published in 1954 as *A Philosophy of the Real and the Possible;* they are miscellaneous rather than systematic, but, like most of his writings, display wit and intellectual virtuosity. His other book was the annotated list of *Books for a College Student's Reading,* which went into five editions. Its dogmatic, pithy criticisms reveal a marked acuteness. For some years he was attached to the reviewing staff of the *Journal of Philosophy.* He submitted notices which, while often mischievous in tone, were deliberate and penetrating. At Trinity he became Professor Emeritus in 1956 but never retired as a teacher. He died suddenly on January 25, 1960. For over thirty-nine years he had made his home in a cluttered suite of two rooms at the college. No close relatives survived him. A brief memoir by R. K. Morris, with a portrait, appeared in the *Trinity College Alumni Magazine* of March, 1960.

Costello's associates agree that he was a voracious reader, for whom a book a day was standard fare; that, from his youth, he secluded himself to the point of eccentricity; that he sported an "almost puckish" sense of humor, capable of wit but tending towards broadness; and that, above all, he showed himself to be a complex and orderly thinker. At Harvard he seemed indifferent to social life and spent his off-hours in the philosophy library at Emerson Hall. But a bookish man must husband his independence. Costello was aloof rather than misanthropic; at Trinity, when he encountered an old colleague on the path, he might stare ahead and merely crook a finger in passing, but the gesture was good-humored, even amiable. When he wished, he could be convivial, and he delighted in watching football games and in listening to academic gossip. His habit of detachment could appear tactless, it was so matter-of-fact:

as a guest in the house of friends, he might survey the dinner table, point to one dish after another with the remark, "I will not eat that," or "I will eat this," and at the last have dined simply on meat and potatoes. To behave thus bluntly seems, at best, like a way of saying, "I know that you know that I know better, and you know that I know that you know it's all one."

If, at a faculty meeting, he sat rocked with silent laughter, it was not from arrogance, though he himself could rise to sort out the issues with incisive clarity and with command of the practical application of ideas. His usual want of zeal did not result from lethargy; if stirred to anger, as by some threat of academic high-handedness, he could give battle. His laughter, often "dead-pan," lacked warmth; it was sly, without rancor. He made slang a style. His praise was rare and uneffusive. He was prone to caricature even those whom he esteemed, such as his old teachers Royce and Santayana. In his own classes he held his distance, not using Royce's maieutic method, but he freely helped his students and took pride in counting up how many of them rose to departmental chairmanships.

His failure to write a synthesis of his philosophy was intentional, for he often said that one had to learn philosophy from a teacher, not from a book; it was also constitutional, owing to a mind which spent itself in meticulous inquiries. It was very like him that, as Leal A. Headley has recalled, he should once have computed *pro rata* how much Royce was paid for each hour in the classroom. Costello was a man of details rather than of large simplifications, and he was not inspired to the act of faith which encourages system-builders.

His powers of close attention and close reasoning ensured that in his notebooks he would record much more than the gist of the proceedings. Though Royces' own notes from earlier years have the unique interest of their authorship, they are drier than Costello's. Being critical minutes, they seek terseness and directness, eliminating detail. They are in fact digests, less elaborate than the summaries prepared away from the seminar by Costello, but otherwise comparable to them except in being impromptu. At that, they are full enough to justify Loewenberg's impression of Royce's careful reporting. It is only when compared with Costello's notes that they seem meager. Royce would seldom try to set down statistical or technical evidence cited in the papers; Costello tried to acknowledge almost every point, so that in his haste he resorted to elliptical phrasing. If this has often teased the curiosity of the editor, it detracts nothing from Costello's accomplishment, namely to have captured, even though in tantalizing snatches, the tones of discussion. The talk had at times an almost Socratic texture, though he was heedless of its form—slipping from the first person into the third and back again.

Now and again he would suffer an off-day, not because of matter, biochemistry or psychiatry being as tractable as logic, but because of some puzzling element in the exposition of the subject, or perhaps because he was tired. What he got revealed him. So far as his task of summarizing was concerned, he need not have taken down a single word of discussion or opinion, but he was avid of what he could learn. One man with intelligence is worth ten with tape-recorders. He never missed a flash of the comic, and he treasured every saying that verged on the unconventional. He moderated the formality of his summaries with scattered witticisms. His supplementary comments underscore the remark of his Trinity colleague Odell Shepard, that to observe Costello was to be made forcibly aware of "a mind working."

During the academic year 1913–14, Royce's seminar would assemble every Tuesday evening, from 7:30 to 9:30, in Room C of Emerson Hall. The official class roll for the spring semester carries the notation that the sessions were to be held on Irving Street— that is, evidently, at Royce's house—but his state of health does not appear to have made this necessary. As in the years just before (except 1912–13, when he was at Oxford on leave) the subject of the seminar was comparative methodology in the field of science. Costello jotted down, inside the front cover of his first notebook, a tentative list of topics: Internal Relations, Causality, Implication and

Deduction, Classification of Sciences, Fertility, Induction. All of these were dealt with at least once during the year. Royce did not insist on uniformity among the students' long papers, but he made a point of asking for short papers on set topics, one on description and explanation and one on causality; and nearly all the students wrote these. Three scientific colleagues read accounts of their recent investigations.

Costello's list of the students and visitors is longer than the class roll. It contains the names not only of active participants but of visitors who, in some cases, seldom attended. The latter included JACOB LOEWENBERG (then on the faculty of Wellesley), ARTHUR AND FRANCES R. DEWING (who moved to New Haven soon after the beginning of the year), and a Dr. Long, evidently PERCY WALDRON LONG of the English Department. R. F. A. HOERNLÉ of the University of Durham, then in his first year at Harvard, was present from time to time, and according to Headley contributed shrewdly to certain of the discussions. The guests offering papers were LAWRENCE JOSEPH HENDERSON (1878–1942), ELMER ERNEST SOUTHARD (1876–1920), and FREDERICK ADAMS WOODS (1873–1939), three who were numbered among Royce's constant helpers. Southard had been going to the seminar since before the turn of the century and had presided over it in 1912 when Royce was ill.

Henderson, an Assistant Professor of Biological Chemistry, was investigating the concept of "fitness"; thus in February, 1912, he had reported on fitness in biology. Earlier, in 1909, he had read a paper on catalysis. In 1913 he summed up the conclusions of his book *The Fitness of the Environment,* then newly published. In its sequel, *The Order of Nature* (1917), he was to confront the teleological implications of his fitness theory. His later publications included *Blood* (1928), *Pareto's General Sociology* (1935), and *The Study of Man* (1941).

Southard, the Bullard Professor of Neuropathology at the Harvard Medical School and a Director of the Boston Psychopathic Hospital, as it was to be named, was continuing his researches, started in clinical practice at the Danvers State Hospital, into the

relation between insanity and brain disease. As Costello observes
in his "Recollections," Southard was a masterly amateur chess
player, whose hypothesis that thinking was motor, not sensory (opposed to the belief of such psychologists as Titchener) was supported by his experience of "imageless thought" in blindfold chess.
He later wrote *The Major Divisions of Mental Hygiene* (1916)
and *Shell-Shock and Other Neuropsychiatric Problems* (1919) and
was the co-author of *Neurosyphilis* (1917) and *The Kingdom of
Evils* (1922). His short, brilliant career has been chronicled in
Frederick P. Gay's lucid memoir *The Open Mind: Elmer Ernest
Southard, 1876–1920* (1938).

Woods was the Curator of Portuguese History at the Harvard
College Library. He had become an Instructor in Comparative His-
tology at the Harvard Veterinary School after taking the M.D. in
1898. That school was discontinued in 1901, and he continued as an
embryologist and histologist at the Harvard Medical School. In
1903, he moved to the Massachusetts Institute of Technology as a
Lecturer. From research in embryology he had transferred his emphasis to heredity and then to the statistical plotting of inheritable
traits. His *Mental and Moral Heredity in Royalty: A Statistical
Study in History and Psychology* (1906) was written in rebuttal
to environmentalism. Its method, which he called historiometry,
evoked a spontaneous letter of praise from Charles S. Peirce. A further study, *The Influence of Monarchs*, appearing in 1913, formed
the context of his reports to the seminar that year.

Of the eleven students originally registered for the seminar of
1913–14, nine were at Harvard and two at Radcliffe. One, ROBERT
L. M. UNDERHILL, a member of the previous year's seminar conducted in Royce's absence by C. M. Bakewell of Yale University,
withdrew early in the term. Another, MARION COATS (later Mrs.
Clifford L. Graves) was there only up to mid-November, when she
went abroad, and she did not resume attendance until May, 1914.
She was a Vassar graduate who had left Yale for Radcliffe in 1911
to study under Royce and who at his invitation had visited the
seminar in 1911–12. In 1914–15 she served as Royce's graduate

assistant. She afterwards became in succession the principal of Ferry Hall Academy and of Bradford Academy, and was the first President of Sarah Lawrence College (1927–1929). The nine who remained throughout the year (the name of one newcomer in the spring semester, J. S. PHILLIPS, was crossed off on the class roll) are listed in Costello's "Recollections." They were as follows:

RALPH MASON BLAKE (1889–1950), A.B. (Williams), 1911; A.M. (Harvard), 1912; Ph.D., 1915. Like his fellow students A. P. Brogan and T. S. Eliot, he had attended Bakewell's seminar. He was inactive in 1913–14. His dissertation was entitled "Hedonism in the Light of Modern Discussions in the Theory of Value." He taught philosophy at Princeton, Wells, and the University of Washington, and, from 1930 until his death, at Brown University.

ALBERT PERLEY BROGAN (1889–   ), A.B. (Harvard), 1911; A.M., 1912; Ph.D., 1914. He wrote his dissertation under Royce on "The Problem of Intrinsic Value." In 1914 he was appointed Instructor in Philosophy at the University of Texas, remaining there to become at length Professor, and, in 1936, the Dean of the Graduate School (now Dean Emeritus). He has published numerous technical and critical papers in the field of values.

THOMAS STEARNS ELIOT, O. M. (1888–   ), A.B. (Harvard), 1910; A.M., 1911. After undergraduate courses in philosophy under Palmer and Santayana, he had studied under Bergson in 1910–11. For the next three years he was in graduate residence at Harvard. He spent 1914–15 at Merton College, Oxford, preparing a monograph on F. H. Bradley. He edited *The Criterion*, 1922–1939, and held the Charles Eliot Norton Professorship of Poetry at Harvard, 1932–33, returning in 1950 to give the Theodore Spencer Memorial Lecture. His works in verse, notably "Prufrock," "The Waste Land," "Ash Wednesday," "Burnt Norton," and the great drama "Murder in the Cathedral," have been collected as *The Complete Poems and Plays* (1952). Additional verse plays have been produced and published. He is the author of many critical essays. He has received various honorary citations and degrees, and in 1948 he was awarded the Nobel Prize for Literature.

LEAL AUBREY HEADLEY (1884–   ), S.B. (Carleton), 1907; A.M. (Harvard), 1910; Ph.D., 1916. He had taught school in Minnesota before coming to Harvard, where he did research on teleology and wrote his dissertation on "The Concept of Purpose." Afterwards for many years until his retirement he was a member of the Philosophy Department at Carleton. His writings include *How To Study in College* (1926) and *Making the Most of Books* (1932).

SAMUEL GRING HEFELBOWER (1871–1950), A.B. (Gettysburg), 1891; A.M., 1894; graduate, the Lutheran Theological Seminary, Gettysburg, 1894; Ph.D. (Harvard), 1914. He had taught German and history at Gettysburg and from 1904 to 1910 had been the President of the college. He was a member of Royce's seminar in 1911–12. He later taught philosophy at Washburn and at Carthage, and religion and philosophy at Wagner (1936–1947). He was given honorary degrees by Dickinson and by Gettysburg. His dissertation, *The Relation of John Locke to English Deism*, was published in 1918, and his *History of Gettysburg College* in 1932.

NARENDRA NATH SEN GUPTA (1889–1944), A.B. (Harvard), 1913; A.M., 1914; Ph.D., 1915. His dissertation was entitled "Anti-intellectualism: A Study in Contemporary Epistemology." He continued in the seminar through 1914–15. He joined the faculty of the University of Calcutta and there organized the first psychology laboratory in India. His offices included the presidency of the Indian Psychological Association and the editorship of the *Indian Journal of Psychology*. From 1929 until his death he was Professor of Philosophy at Lucknow University. He published psychological and philosophical articles and was the coauthor of *Introduction to Social Psychology* (1928).

LEONARD THOMPSON TROLAND (1889–1932), S.B. (M.I.T.), 1912; A.M. (Harvard), 1914; Ph.D., 1915. At Harvard he won the Bowdoin Prize for Chemistry (1914). After submitting his dissertation, "Studies of Visual Equilibria," he spent a year in optical research for the General Electric Company. He then went back to Harvard and taught psychology there until almost the end of his life, concurrently holding engineering posts—for the United States Navy

during the first World War, in the development of submarine listening devices; for Kalmus, Comstock, and Westcott, Inc. (1918–
1925); and for the Technicolor Motion Picture Corporation (1918–
1932), latterly as director of research and process control. He was a
co-inventor of the Technicolor process. With D. F. Comstock he
wrote *The Nature of Matter and Electricity* (1917), and was the
author of *The Present State of Visual Science* (1922), *The Mystery
of Mind* (1926), *The Fundamentals of Human Motivation* (1928),
and *The Principles of Psychophysiology*, in four volumes (1929–
1932).

BENJAMIN WHITMAN VAN RIPER (1885–1955), A.B. (Alle-
gheny), 1905; Ph.D. (Boston University), 1908; Ph.D. (Chicago),
1912. While attending the seminar, he belonged to the faculty of
Boston University, to which he had come from Nebraska Wesleyan
in 1912. He had turned to philosophy after taking the advanced degree in psychology, and he studied at Jena and Paris after leaving
Harvard. He afterwards taught at Pennsylvania State and at Rock-
ford, later withdrawing from the academic profession. From 1934
to 1948 he worked as the public relations secretary in the Chicago
office of Carleton College. His Chicago dissertation, *Some Views of
the Time Problem*, appeared in 1916.

FLORENCE WEBSTER (1889–   ), A.B. (Wellesley), 1912; A.M.,
1915; Ph.D. (Columbia), 1922. Miss Webster was at Radcliffe from
1912 to 1914 and in 1916–17. She has held no academic appoint-
ments. Her doctoral dissertation at Columbia, *The Nature of Life:
A Study in Metaphysical Analysis*, published in 1922, was developed out of researches for her Wellesley thesis, "A Conception of
Life," for which she had prepared the groundwork while in Royce's
seminar.

The notebooks filled up by Costello, sitting on Royce's right with
all the participants in view around the seminar table, most of them
busy with their own note-taking, remained in his possession when
he left Harvard. They had served their purpose, but Costello kept
them. Later he forgot about them. For years he was accustomed to
echo (and to exaggerate) in reviews or lectures the more striking

sallies of Royce, but for these he drew on memory. The notebooks lay in obscurity until, after almost four decades, he found them again. In the final weeks of his life Costello recounted to Max H. Fisch how the discovery was made: "When a shed on the back of my property in Richmond, Indiana, was torn down to build a garage, I was brought a dust-covered box. It contained my Harvard notes and papers which I had forgotten, including two stout notebooks on [Royce's] seminar. I opened at random and found Royce and Eliot in debate." Delighted with this trove, which caused him to think of "Malahide Castle and the croquet box," Costello took the notebooks with him to Trinity College. In December, 1952, while on a stroll near Washington Square in New York, he mentioned them to Houston Peterson of Rutgers, who had once been a student of his at Columbia. Three years later, during a visit by Peterson to Trinity, he remembered Peterson's interest and turned them over to him. This was shortly before the Royce centenary, for which Costello had readied the paper "Recollections of Royce's Seminar on Comparative Methodology." Peterson is mainly responsible for the attention paid to them since that time.

These notebooks, so far as is known, present the only surviving contemporary account of the seminar as it was in 1913–14. Costello never tampered with their form and spent no time substantiating references or correcting factual errors. After their rediscovery, he could not have done much to expand his notes on the discussions, though he might have further annotated the papers. His record of the discussions, however sketchy, is at least a unique feature, not paralleled in the unpublished Lenzen notebooks for a later period, which are now in the Archives of the University of California at Berkeley. The material in the papers remains of course largely available either in articles or in dissertations, though this is not true, for instance, of the papers read by T. S. Eliot. (In a letter to the present editor, in 1949, Eliot said that his paper on the methodology of anthropology had not been preserved. A courteous attempt to gain more information has proved to be wasted, but it is likely that Eliot's other papers no longer exist if that one does not.)

In any case the papers are not equivalent to the seminar, whose human transactions at the time come to light only in Costello's minutes. Costello agreed that the notebooks should be published, but he was unwilling to edit them himself. What he would have had to do with them, in order to satisfy his critical judgment, looked like far too big a task at so many years' distance from the seminar. He said that they contained too much of his own opinions; he would have wanted to change them into something more objective. What he would have felt obliged to do, however, differed radically from what anyone else could feel licensed to do; and it was rather paradoxical that, after all, he gave Peterson and the Rutgers University Press a free hand in choosing how and under whose editorship they should be published. The editor, having been given a free hand in his own turn, has abandoned any thought of transforming the notebooks as Costello might have liked to do and has been content to keep, with no significant exceptions, the rough immediacy that Costello might have sacrificed.

❧ JOSIAH ROYCE'S SEMINAR, 1913-1914

❧ EDITOR'S FOREWORD TO THE TEXT

The intelligibility of Costello's rapid notes improves as one becomes familiar with the matters sifted in them. It might be found helpful if, after examining the notes of the orientation meeting, the reader went on at once to the various formal summaries. At quite an early stage, however, it should be rewarding to study the notes and summaries comparatively. The summaries, though alone in developing Costello's views on the topics and on the participants, all but lack the moment-to-moment dramatic vividness of his extempore jottings: the pulse of the seminar beats most strongly there. In the notes, too, occur many factual details which are missing from the summaries. By making frequent cross-references the reader can gain multiplied evidence of the sharpness and subtlety of Costello's mind while witnessing with him, at as close quarters as now may be, the active genius of Josiah Royce.

For obvious reasons the notes have called for a larger apparatus of editorial commentary than the summaries; in order to keep this from proliferating unduly in one respect, the editor has left to the Index of Proper Names at the end of the volume the function of removing any possible ambiguities among the many citations of philosophers and scientists.

September 30, 1913

🐦 NOTES

Nineteen present.

Royce: On purpose of seminary. Methods in general. Much value in comparing methods of diverse sciences. Former seminaries on concepts, e.g., aggregates. Recently methods have been more profitable. Example of Professor Reisner.[1] Use of hypotheses. Statistics. Certain directing concepts. Dr. Woods, *The Influence of Monarchs*. Cf. Preface, statistical methods. Professor Henderson, *The Fitness of the Environment*. Concept of "fitness." [2]

Professor Henderson explains his notion of fitness, an unsymmetrical reciprocal relation. Fitness of matter for any sort of mechanism or phenomenon in general. Define mechanism (physical-chemical terms).

Royce: Danger of over-generalization.

Professor Henderson: Concept of system (a material group in space).

Activity of system.

Duration of system.

All characters of system.

[1] According to one of Royce's notebooks, G. A. Reisner, Assistant Professor of Egyptology, spoke in the seminar on December 5, 1911, concerning archaeological methods.

[2] Woods' *The Influence of Monarchs: Steps in a New Science of History* (New York, 1913) and Henderson's *The Fitness of the Environment: An Inquiry into the Biological Significance of the Properties of Matter* (New York, 1913) provided major topics of discussion for the rest of the year.

Fitness for any mechanism.

Fitness means favorable to great variety of mechanisms.

Gibbs: components, phases, concentration, temperature.

Energy needed.

Duration depends on constancy of conditions.

Dr. Woods: Heredity and environment, problem of separating.

Next, October 7: Royce, concept of "fitness." October 14: Dr. Woods, heredity and environment. October 21: Professor Henderson, For what is physical world fit? October 28: Professor Southard.

Royce wishes later to discuss a new formal operation. Mr. Troland will discuss relativity without mathematics.

Royce: Chasles said future mathematics would make things so clear they could be explained to a friend on the street. Clifford and Maxwell.

October 7, 1913

ࡠ NOTES

[*Royce*]:

Ordinal functions: [3]

$$g = abc + \overline{abc} + a\overline{bd} + \overline{abd}$$
$$h = abd + \overline{abd} + a\overline{bc} + \overline{abc}$$

$$\overline{}$$

$$a = cdg + \overline{cdg} + c\overline{dh} + \overline{cdh}$$
$$b = cdh + \overline{cdh} + c\overline{dg} + \overline{cdg}$$

$$a\overline{b} + \overline{a}b = c$$
$$b\overline{c} + \overline{b}c = a$$
$$a\overline{c} + \overline{a}c = b$$

The number concept is familiar but abstract. Laws of commutation and association. Why are certain operations commutative, etc.? In number the inverse operations are always possible. Commutation plus association plus invertibility equals group character. Sym-

[3] The following summarizes Royce's "An Extension of the Algebra of Logic," *Journal of Philosophy*, X (November 6, 1913), 617–33.

metry of structure results. Space has such symmetry, hence number, etc., can be applied to it. Symmetries of a crystal illustrate a group.

Analogies of classes or propositions, and numbers. Logical classification is dual (a and ā). Nothing corresponds in number. Sums and products in logic are associative and commutative but not invertible. Boolean and ordinary algebra: theory of equations (in Boolean you can solve all). Boolean analysis, by Peano, etc., of complex reasoning but not fertile in novelty. "Boolean entities" are various, not classes only. Other algebras, e.g., quaternions. Combinations of algebras, e.g., theory of complex variables. Whitehead says Boolean algebra is like argon. Fractions are "directed pairs of whole numbers." Complex numbers are pairs also. Pairs have far different properties from their constituents. Same is true of triads. Is there an algebra where two pairs determine the third in a group? *Hereupon:*

Consider ordinal functions defined. Then if g and h are defined, a and b can be found in terms of cdgh; invertible. [Given] $\frac{a}{b} \circ \frac{c}{d} = \frac{g}{h}$; then o is commutative and invertible. Same property as in rational fractions. $\frac{g}{h} \circ \frac{d}{c} = \frac{a}{b}$ or $\frac{g}{h} \circ \frac{b}{a} = \frac{c}{d}$. There is a unity here. $\frac{a}{b} \circ \frac{1}{1} = \frac{a}{b}$ where 1 = universe. Order the central mathematical concept. Logical entities have a certain order (Kempe).

$$\frac{a}{b} \circ \frac{a}{b} = \left(\frac{a}{b}\right)^2 = \frac{ab + \overline{a}\overline{b}}{\overline{a}b + a\overline{b}}.$$

$$\left(\frac{a}{b}\right)^3 = \frac{b}{a}.$$

$$\left(\frac{a}{b}\right)^4 = \frac{1}{1}.$$

$$\left(\frac{a}{b}\right)^5 = \frac{a}{b}.$$

Fitness: Concrete problem; question is to "get the right abstraction." Henderson's book. Physical world we have is best possible environment for organisms. Is this the old design argument? No. Can we generalize the concept of fitness without metaphysical preconceptions? Fitness is likely to suggest purpose (*als ob*). What is the differentia of purpose here? Organic unity suggests purpose, but this is itself obscure. Kant's *Urteilskraft* is too rigid, one uniform faculty of the mind. What is the law and order of this system and (1) where does the exception come into the system? (If nominalism were true, all things would be exceptions.) When are exceptions important? (Cf. singular points of a curve, piston's velocity at end of a stroke, tire of a wheel touches the ground, explosions, etc.) Exceptions often suggest purpose. (2) Events have values. To determine objective value is very difficult. Value would cease often were it merely subjective. Suppose exceptional fact coincident with an objective value: this is a fitness. Concept of fitness does not apply to a total system. No question of mind here involved. (Much depends for our astronomy on fact that moon in eclipse just about covers the sun. Case of fitness—*als ob*. Star—Algol variable type. Any group of living beings.) Fitness does not imply purpose. What brought about that fitness is still a question. (1) Purpose is only one way of explaining it. (2) Objective chance is another explanation. (Chance is not non-causation, chance is a statistical concept. Law determines twenty per thousand die, chance determines what individual.) (3) Darwinian hypotheses. Concept of a "trap" interested Professor James. Natural selection produces an apparent fitness. (4) Quasi-psychological or animistic, vitalistic explanation. Blind strivings, trial and error, e.g., in comparative psychology. Bergson's *élan vital*.

Professor Henderson has discovered a fitness. Not due to "chance." Not a "trap," no natural selection. Not vitalistic, Bergsonian, because value and fitness appear much later. Design argument (Paley) not adequate. Chronosynoptic: e.g., coincidence appears in case of inventor of hypotheses, mind is "attuned." Case of logical entities which finally seem to show fitness.

October 7, 1913

ຂ SUMMARY

Professor Royce presented a discussion (monologue!) of two topics rather distinct from one another: the one a new development of
the algebra of logic, the other a definition of the concept of "fitness."
In the first, he remarked that the operations of ordinary algebra
have the group character: they are associative, commutative, and
invertible, and have a symmetry of structure which finds a concrete analogue in the symmetries, for example, of a crystal.

In the Boolean algebra of logic, operations are not invertible in
any general way, and this is, in part at least, the reason why
Boolean algebra lacks the richness of novel developments which
characterizes ordinary algebra and mathematical algebras generally. Professor Royce believes he has found, within the field of
Boolean algebra, a possible development of an algebra of pairs
of logical entities which possess that fertility which the algebra of
single logical entities does not. Given two pairs of logical entities
(which entities may be, for example, classes in a given universe),
certain combinations of these pairs determine a third pair. This
combination of two pairs constitutes the chief operation of the system, and it is found to be invertible, with striking analogies to the
operations on ordinary rational numbers, the "fractions." Moreover, if we duplicate the same pair instead of taking different pairs
in applying our operation; that is, if we perform an operation
similar to raising to a power, the third power turns out to be the

reciprocal of the pair thus "cubed," and the fourth power is the $\frac{1}{1}$

pair, the modulus. These curious properties are not duplicated in
any other algebra.

The question about a new algebra is highly abstract. The question of the nature of fitness goes rather to the other extreme of concreteness; the problem is, indeed, to get from it the *right abstraction*. In Professor Henderson's book on *The Fitness of the Environment*, the thesis advanced is that the material world is the best possible environment for organisms. This is not necessarily a mere revival of the old design argument, but to show that it is not, it becomes necessary to define what is meant by "fitness" in such a way as to free it from teleological, and indeed all metaphysical, preconceptions. Yet it is always *as if* there were purpose involved in any case of fitness. Kant's appeal to a rigid mental faculty (*Urteilskraft*) scarcely furnishes an explanation of this appearance of purpose which is flexible enough for the diversity of cases of apparent fitness.

Two factors are, however, found in all such cases, and these suffice to give us a definition. The first is the existence of exceptions. Even where a strict law prevails, often certain cases under that law will have an exceptional character (e.g., singular points on a curve, points of halting or sudden change in a physical process). Secondly, we may note, that we suppose our judgments of value frequently to report something more than a mere subjective preference; that there are, in some sense, objective values. Suppose an exception coincident with some such imputed objective value, then we have what we call a "fitness," something which seems to us as if it were designed. Examples are the astronomical value of solar eclipses or Algol variables, cases as if prepared for the instruction of the astronomer.

Fitness, then, is a coincidence of the exceptional case with an objective value. But where such fitnesses are numerous, the question forces itself to the front, What brought them about? (1) We may say it was purpose. (2) We may say it was objective chance. (3) We may say it was Darwinian survival, or perhaps selection by what Professor James called a "trap," which, like the pile of driftwood, once started, grows by selecting automatically other floating particles. (4) We may give a quasi-psychological explanation in terms of blind strivings and trial and error, Bergson's *élan vital*.

Professor Henderson has discovered a sort of fitness holding between the environment and all life. But to it none of the explanations apply. Paley's design argument does not really explain scientifically. And the fitness in question is too general to be due to chance coincidence. Nor, apparently, is it attributable to natural selection. The Bergsonian blind strivings channeling out matter do not explain it, for here was a preparation for life long before life came. It is this last point, the "chronosynoptic" character of the fitness, the vast range of time involved, which makes Professor Henderson's problem so puzzling.

Professor Royce closed with a mention of certain other examples of fitness: the way in which, at times, the mind of the scientific discoverer seems "attuned" with the natural world, and again, the strange agreements between diverse entities which surprise one in the realms of logical and mathematical form.

I have only one comment to add: The criticism of Bergson seemed to emphasize a side of Bergson's doctrine which is not the one here most relevant. Doubtless there are those present who know Bergson much better than I, and indeed I speak less from a close study of his writings than from contact with the man. I heard him, however, in a lecture on the "Concept of Evolution," lay down, first of all, two theses as the fundamental ones, ones whose neglect brought about the failure, e.g., of Spencer's interpretation of evolution. First, rest is to be interpreted in terms of motion, structure by function, and so on. And secondly, the past must not be interpreted in terms of the present, particularly as regards the so-called lower forms of existence. The second point is the one relevant to our topic. A sharp dualism exists at the present time, says Bergson, between life and the dead matter to which it gives form. And we say dead matter has always been here, and life must have sprung from dead matter, somehow, by some miracle. That is wrong. Evolution is always fanlike, always diverging both ways from a common origin. Where there is a dualism now, both sides have sprung from a somewhat which had in it the potentialities of both. Life did not come late and find an alien matter somehow fit for it. Life and matter were once of the same stock, which was neither the one nor the other but something somewhere between them both. Such is the Bergsonian interpretation. I do not myself defend this doctrine, I simply say that this is the side of Bergson's philosophy which is relevant to the issue presented.

October 14, 1913

ॐ NOTES

[?*Royce*]:   There are many Boolean examples.

Henderson: Bergson uses certain postulates of energy which are true but not the only truths. Matter is equally important with energy.

Woods: Separating heredity and environment. Many people confused about. In early days environment was the thing. Recently heredity comes to the front, and in a more definite way. Does environment produce a change in the individual, leaving aside the question of acquired characteristics? Heredity is a law term. Many confused phrases: e.g., *nature and nurture, natal, inborn, blood will tell,* etc. Resemblance between ancestor and offspring is often considered, but there are cases of no resemblance. Since rediscovery of Mendel's laws: what is in the germ cell? There are cases clearly contrasted, fishes and frogs, black and white rabbits. Mendelian explanation. Was *there,* in the primary cells. Differences between individuals which are foreshadowed in the germ cell. Practical question is the one here. In applying fertilizers, etc., one does influence through environment. Examples of human heredity. Difference of eye color is due to heredity, not the color itself. Language is due to environment. Jukes family are no proof of heredity.

Galton's study of twins and of men of genius [in *Inquiries into Human Faculty and Its Development*]. Case of royalty eliminates difference of environment, as of social classes. Cases of maternal grandfather. Dr. Laporte [i.e., C. B. Davenport?] (Cold Spring Harbor) has data of half brothers with different fathers, compared with brothers with same fathers. Thorndike's studies of twins [in *Measurements of Twins*] (correlation .90 or so). Just as many younger sons rose to distinction as did elder brothers, so here environment did not affect. Thorndike on question of addition. Equal training of clever and less clever men. Education makes men more unlike. Women today more often achieve fame—environment. If Germany has increased in scientific power more than in numbers, that is environment. Old World and New, do lower classes produce more famous men? No. Pearson has given one good case: tuberculosis, brothers vs. husband and wife [in E. G. Pope's *A Second Study of the Statistics of Pulmonary Tuberculosis*]. Constitutional factor more important than had been thought.—*Amen.*

Royce: Statistical application of [Mill's] agreement and difference.

Southard: How about insanity in Massachusetts? [4]

Woods: Mountains and sea, etc.

Southard found valley towns good, hilltops bad. Berkshires and islands good, but some towns show same environment and different heredity.

Woods: You don't in such cases know enough about heredity.

Southard: Towns (0–20) vary more than cities (3.5–10).

Royce: More famous men in Massachusetts. But there are opportunities as well as heredity.

Woods: This had no bearing on the question. In question of

---

4 Cf. Southard, "Note on the Geographical Distribution of Insanity in Massachusetts, 1901–1910," *Boston Medical and Surgical Journal*, CLXVI (March 28, 1912), 479–83; "Second Note on the Geographical Distribution of Mental Disease in Massachusetts, 1901–1910: The Insanity-Rates of the Smaller Cities," *Boston Medical and Surgical Journal*, CLXIX (August 28, 1913), 302–06.

America and Europe, we find the environment does not influence in this case, as regards notable relatives. On *Nation.* !!!*?!!! [5]

Royce: Problems of *The Influence of Monarchs* and germ plasm vs. environment. On reviewers (omniscience, condescension). Difficulties of special problems. Case of cancer? Negative results.

Woods: Rare diseases seem hereditary. Probably cancer also. Pearson says if one explanation will do, parsimony will demand you use it.

October 14, 1913

ह SUMMARY

Dr. Woods read a paper on the possibility of separating heredity and environment. He explicitly confined his attention to the individual, leaving to one side the question of "acquired characters." The individual is influenced by environment and also by heredity; and the question is, how to find cases where the amount of influence due to each can be separately estimated. Any particular trait will, in its absolute amount, be due to both causes, but where a number of individuals differ relatively as regards a given trait, if in such cases heredity is approximately the same, the relative variation is probably due to environment, and *vice versa.*

The inquiry suffers from various disadvantages: e.g. the vagueness of our conceptions of just what heredity and environment should be defined to be; or again, the difficulty of finding cases where one factor is clearly constant. Our first results may, nevertheless, be of some practical value, even though they may in some respects need later revision.

Examples of such investigations are: (1) Galton's study of twins

[5] Woods was fulminating against the unsympathetic review of *The Influence of Monarchs* in the *Nation,* XCVII (October 9, 1913), 341–42.

and (2) of men of genius; (3) Dr. Woods' own study of royalty; (4) Dr. Laporte's [sic] study of half brothers; (5) Thorndike's studies of twins and (6) of powers of arithmetical addition (in which latter case the same training made men less alike); (7) Pearson's work on tuberculosis. Then there are the cases of (8) the relation of women to fame; (9) causes of scientific progress in Germany; (10) comparison of the Old and New Worlds—all of them cases where environmental influences might be studied, etc. With this enumeration, Dr. Woods ended his presentation.

Professor Southard asked how far the same method could be applied to the determination of causes of insanity in Massachusetts, and various suggestions were advanced as to how to attack this problem. Dr. Woods said each special problem demands a special method, but probably in this case he should begin with a study of the heredity of the insane, rather than with their environment.

Professor Royce pointed out that Dr. Woods' book on *The Influence of Monarchs* was less a study of monarchy than it was of heredity. Professor Royce also asked about the heredity of cancer. Dr. Woods replied that since rare diseases seem largely hereditary, it is probable that the more frequent ones are hereditary also, or at least to a larger degree than is ordinarily supposed.

This discussion, along with some remarks by Professor Royce on the "omniscience and condescension" of reviewers (which remarks doubtless also fit the reviewer of the present seminary), brought the meeting to a close.

I should like now to "condescend" to a few remarks on the place of Dr. Woods' method among scientific methods generally. Agreement and difference, the methods of Mill's Canons, seem to be used today less as a method of proof for induction proper than as a method of discovery in certain more or less statistical inquiries. Dr. Woods' method seems to be a special case of what I shall call, for want of a better term, "statistical inductions." A "statistical induction" may perhaps be best described as involving not an "inductive leap" from known to unknown cases, but an analysis of certain cases, all of them known in their general features, but so complex as to baffle complete direct analysis. It is an analysis which proceeds by classifying a great number of such cases according to some principle p, and then according to some other principle q. If the resultant classifications are similar, that is fall, into parallel groups or parallel series, we infer p is significantly related to q. Of course, the more analytically we know our cases to begin with, the fewer cases we need.

A clear and typical example of the method in question is Campbell's investigations at the Lick Observatory. He classified stars by velocity. He then classified them by spectroscopic age. He found the classifications fell into a sort of one-one correspondence, with the same star at approximately the same place in each classification. He then inferred a relation to exist between velocity and age; older stars move faster, a result which was entirely unanticipated.

It seems to me Dr. Woods' method is best grouped as a variant of the method just described. In Dr. Woods' method we have three principles of possible classification: the trait to be examined, heredity, and environment, which we may call p, q, and q' respectively. We choose, then, a group of cases where, say, q' gives no characteristic classification; e.g., the environment is uniform or else varied at random. By a "characteristic" classification I mean one which gives to the objects classified a marked and definite order. If, in the hypothetical example, q' gives no characteristic but instead a random classification, while p and q give characteristic classifications which correspond, or if the trait differs as heredity differs, we infer that p and q are connected, that the variations of the trait in question have their basis in hereditary differences.

This characterization of all such "statistical inductions" as a comparison of classifications in order to infer what relations, if any, hold between the selected principles of classification, may seem unnecessarily abstract, but I think that only so can we show clearly what such methods have in common, and the formulation will include Mill's Canons almost as a special case. But we must notice that a "statistical induction" is an analysis, and not an inference from observed to unobserved cases of the same kind. One value of "statistical induction" is that, though dealing with a somewhat complex subject-matter, it makes no prior hypothesis about the particular question it wishes to solve. It simply classifies cases by their known qualities, and is then able to infer with probability a previously unknown relation between those qualities.

October 21, 1913

ࣝ NOTES

[*Royce*]: Egyptian archaeology and also philology. Wiener. Series-type discovery of laws and causal connection. No hypothesis. Close up your series.[6] Minot says the same in embryology ("Best proof known to me").

Woods: [That] one can do more with lower organisms by "environmental persuasion," is a prediction which might follow, but need not. Hypotheses often come in, but statistics must come in.

Royce: Important thing is that a certain combination could not have come by chance.

Troland: Holt's function-conception of causality.

Henderson: Summary of book [*The Fitness of the Environment*]. Fitness of environment is as important as of organism. This is the fittest environment. Since Darwin, problem has been evaded. Complexity and durability of organism presupposed regulation of environment. A living being must exchange matter and energy with environment.

In what degree are carbon, hydrogen, oxygen present in the proper amount and combination everywhere? Rich and exact infor-

---

[6] Leo Wiener, Assistant Professor of Slavic Languages and Literatures, addressed the seminar on October 17, 1911, concerning the philological importance of each separate stage in the development of a word. A closed-up series would show all stages.

mation. Specific heat, solubility, coefficient of expansion, etc. Constant temperature of ocean, richness of carbon compounds, etc. Would not ammonia and silicon do as well? Proof that they [would] not will be offered. Constant temperature of ocean is due to high specific heat of water. Water holds many things in solution, hence ocean gives food. Cf. solvent power of water in blood, lymph, etc. Energy required to liberate hydrogen and oxygen is great, heat of combustion of hydrogen is maximal. Hence energy furnished to organism is very great. Other bodies do not possess such properties as H_2O, etc. Reciprocal relations, not symmetrical, of organism (special adaptation) and environment (general fitness). No other environment of known elements could be so fit.

Objections (J. A. Thomson, [review] in *The Hibbert Journal*, [1913]): Evidence insufficient. Tendency to complexify. "The earth is friendly to living creatures because . . . they are bone of her bone." (1) Peculiar fitnesses but not a maximum of fitness. Highest specific heat does give maximum regulation, etc. The only question is, What is it fittest for? Thomson argues we can't imagine other forms of life and hence there is no real question. (The physical scientists have not objected as regards organisms.) (2) Adapted to what they are adapted to.

It is not organic evolution that has made organisms durable, complex with metabolism, for even the simplest organism has [this].

Does a world of matter-energy-space-time impose any limitations on mechanisms arising therein? Gibbs' "phase-rule" is the only answer. Concept of a "material system," an aggregate of matter, isolated, occupying a portion of space. Every physical thing is a system or a part of one. Matter-space. There remains energy-time? Every system has activity, hence energy. It has also duration. Form, size, physical and chemical constituents, energy transformations, and duration are the things to look for. These are the fundamental characteristics of system plus energy plus duration. (1) The "phases," (2) components (chemical individuals), (3) concentration, (4) temperature, (5) pressure. A phase is any homogeneous part. Maxima of possible phases and components, and varieties of concentrations increase possible variety of phenomena. So also maximum of mobility increases number of systems. So, since many are unstable, regulation will increase number possible. A mechanism is an active system. So also variety increased by energy changes and chemical varieties. Mobility of water greatest, e.g., vapor tension rapidly changeable. Solvent power of water maximal, hence greater variety of possible components brought together. Temperature, pressure, concentration, acidity or alkalinity of water. Close to maximal. So also heat of combination, etc. Hence more energy available. Carbon, hydrogen, oxygen give greater possibility of energy transformations. The environment is fittest for any mechanism, i.e., the greatest number of mechanisms.

Troland's criticism: Coincidences of properties must have *fewer* antecedent causes.

[*Henderson*]: This is not a destructive criticism. All the maxima are favorable, and this is not to be explained; it is a fitness.

Royce: A fitness is the coincidence of an exceptional case with a value. An enduring and rich life has more value because of its duration and richness. Professor Henderson's account fits the definition. If elements evolved, this is an exceptional production of maxima. No answer to say: "Of course world is fit for whatever it produced."

Henderson: Real question: Do the special characteristics of environment fit the environment for those general characteristics of organisms imposed by general characteristics of environment?

Troland: Values not involved. Environment not what is outside but what preceded and caused. Henderson a posteriori. But why not a priori? Causally determined system, hence any preceding state must be a maximum of such as to produce the following. In any causal system the earlier state is [the] maximum fit to produce a later state.

Royce: Wundt said once teleology is cause read the other way. Teleology generally is taken to mean design. Our question is, Is there a third possibility, an objective concept of fitness? Yes, where coincidences do not necessarily follow from the general laws, so far as we know. World might be causal without being as it actually is.

Henderson: Value comes in notion of *any*, i.e. variety and number.

Brogan: You need a theory of objective values.

Henderson: Food values!

Royce: Say "interesting fact." Objective values do not need a theory, they are facts.

Henderson: This is a universe of mechanisms, active systems. Reduce the maxima, you diminish the variety and amount of mechanism.

Woods objects to "durability," "complexity," and "metabolism."

Henderson: Natural selection does not explain. Let us find invariants not gained by selection.

Royce: Coincidence needs explanation in a sense in which general laws of nature do not. Familiar comments: (1) Might be other kinds of life. (2) World produces what it produces. Both miss the point. Fitness still remains with us in biology.

[Next]: Southard's subject: Delusions concerning the self, about environment, about *soma*. Classification of delusions. Beliefs, attitudes: pragmatic, not phantastic or intellectual. Motor and sensory brain.

October 21, 1913

ᕗ SUMMARY

In some remarks on the nature of induction at the beginning of the meeting, Professor Royce said that the important thing determined by induction is that a certain combination could not have come about by chance. Some inductions employ hypotheses, but others do not. Examples of the latter class are: the comparison of two classifications to determine if the principles of classification used are significantly related, or again, the process of finding all the members of a series. This latter process of closing up a series by discovering intermediate stages has been insisted upon at previous meetings of the seminary by Professor Wiener, in describing his investigations into the history of words, and by Professor Minot, who said, "It is the best proof known to me in embryology."

After these remarks on induction, Professor Henderson took up the main topic of the evening, the problem raised in his book on *The Fitness of the Environment*. In order that there should exist many organisms which are complex and durable and possessed of powers of metabolism, it is essential that the environment should provide regularity of conditions and a rich supply of energy-yielding foods. Such conditions could be furnished only by an abundance of carbon, hydrogen, and oxygen, and their compounds. It may be shown with a high degree of scientific rigor that these three elements are in more respects close to the maximum of favorableness to the existence of organisms than are any others among the known elements. But it so happens that just these three favorable elements are also the most frequently found. Hence we may conclude that adaptation of organism and environment is a reciprocal, though unsymmetrical, relation, and the present physical world is the fittest possible, of any constituted of the known elements, for the existence of organisms.

Professor Henderson thinks it possible to generalize still further, and say this is true not only as regards organisms but also as regards any sort of mechanisms whatsoever. A mechanism is any active "system," and system may be defined as Gibbs defined it, "an isolated aggregate of matter occupying a portion of space." What we have to consider about systems are: (1) the "phases" (i.e. the number of homogeneous parts), (2) the chemical components, (3) the concentration, (4) the temperature, (5) the pressure, and to these we may add for systems existing in time, (6) the duration, and (7) the energy transformations. The number, variety, and durability of mechanisms increase in direct ratio to the following factors: (1) the number of phases, (2) the number of components,

(3) the varieties of concentrations, (4) the mobility, (5) the regularity of the environment (since many mechanisms are stable only within narrow limits), (6) the number of energy changes, (7) the chemical varieties present, etc. Here again, carbon, hydrogen, and oxygen furnish the maximal favorableness in almost all these respects; and we may conclude that the environment we have is the fittest environment, not only for organisms but for mechanisms in general.

Professor Henderson later stated the specific question here at issue thus: "Do the *special* characteristics of the environment fit the environment for those *general* characteristics which are demanded of organisms (and mechanisms in general) by the *general* matter-energy-space-time characters of the environment, and if so, is there any further explanation for this three-cornered relationship?" At least natural selection does not here explain.

Both Professor Henderson and Professor Royce went over the criticisms advanced against Professor Henderson's position. These criticisms take three forms: (1) This is a revival of the argument from design. (2) The world is fittest to produce what it has produced, and that is the end of the matter. (3) There might be other forms of life than those we know, and for these others, other conditions might be fittest. The first two criticisms miss the real point, and the third is not true in the world we know.

Professor Royce recalled his definition of fitness as the coincidence of an exceptional case with some sort of objective value. Such a fitness we meet with here, and it is not teleology, especially not that sort which is only causality read backwards. Professor Royce's introduction of the concept of value was criticized by some members of the seminary. Mr. Troland said value was irrelevant in physical science, and Mr. Brogan said we needed a general theory of values. Professor Royce replied to the charge of irrelevance that it is just the value in question which first attracts our attention to the problem. The present coincidence is not attributable to chance, and is not explained by simply calling it a case of cause and effect, for the fact that the world is subject to general causal uniformities does not predetermine that it shall have the specific peculiarity here exhibited. It is convenient to define such a fitness in terms of value, but in so doing, no general theory of value is presupposed. With this reply the discussion closed.

Professor Southard promised to present at the next time a sketch of his work in classifying delusions—delusions about the self, etc., also delusions about the environment—with some comment on Professor Henderson's work.

Criticism: I fear any comment I may be able to make on the discussion just summarized will be rather superficial. I will, however, mention two questions which have come to me. Professor Henderson presented us with what is, in part, a proof of a certain thesis, a proof which consists largely in rearranging material already in the possession of science under a new aspect; and secondly, he presented us with a problem for further investigation. The question whether the investigation of a certain problem will yield valuable results is of course one that can never be finally decided except by trial. But the scientist is, nevertheless, guided in his work by a feeling that certain lines of investigation are likely to prove fertile. Scientific answers are judged by their truth or falsity, and concerning the determination of these, much is said in the logical treatises. But scientific questions, of which hypothesis is a special case, are determined by fertility, and concerning the criteria of fertility, or the very mention of such a concept, most logical works are silent. My query is: Is there any criterion as to whether a question will prove fruitful or not, other than the intuition of the individual scientist?

Secondly, I should like to raise the question again, as to in how far a value is needed in defining a "fitness." Could we say we had a fitness or unfitness, when certain exceptional cases, in the sense defined, occurring in a class of objects A led to almost any sort of consequences in another class of objects B? I suppose we might have to measure the consequences in question in terms of some knowledge of the nature of the objects B apart from such influence, or in terms of the resultant number, variety, and durability of the objects B. It may be said this is an evaluation. But I doubt if number and variety are themselves to be called values, though they may be as closely bound up with certain kinds of value as is a particular wave length of light with the color blue. So my second query is this: What is the precise relation of value to fitness; is it only a convenient external sign, or is it more objectively a constituent of the relation of fitness? Both my queries, let it be understood, ask for information rather than urge a criticism.

October 28, 1913

₰ NOTES

[*Royce*]: C. S. Peirce (Harvard 1859) is in seventies. Dr. Woods' letter from Peirce (1906)—*Heredity in Royalty*.[7] "You use logical

---

[7] The reference was to Woods' *Mental and Moral Heredity in Royalty: A Statistical Study in History and Psychology* (New York, 1906). Woods had never heard of Peirce before receiving the letter. It has not been preserved. In 1923 Woods wrote an account of it (now among the Peirce papers in the Houghton Library) in which he explained: "I lent it to a friend to have it copied. He lost it. As near as I can recall the letter was substantially the following. I read it many times and so remember it pretty well. Peirce was staying at the St. Botolph Club at the time, attending a meeting of the National Academy of Sciences. He happened to come across a copy of my *Heredity in Royalty*.—'I have been reading a copy of your new book *Heredity in Royalty* and have been much struck by its correct logic. But on page 287 you appeal to a well-known principle of logic known as the law of parsimony. I deny that a law or principle of logic can be appealed to for support. If you have reasoned correctly you have reasoned logically and need no appeal to authority. All you need to say is: This one cause, heredity, is adequate or nearly adequate. Why introduce more or other causes?' (Etc.) Here follows some fine discussion of 'Occam's Razor.' . . . Peirce then goes on to say that the work would be improved if I had graded the characters according to my own estimates but checked

principle as a premise. I deny that this is valid. Logic cannot supply premises." "Law of parsimony." You should simply reason as logic counsels, appeal to the reason on which logic rests. Royce added [that] to appeal to a logical principle is unnecessary. "Limit of formalism" as mentioned by Russell. Lewis Carroll (Dodgson) in a note in *Mind* [1895], "What the Tortoise said to Achilles": prove by argument that truth of antecedent implies truth of consequent. Common sense says—(Gilbert, *Bab Ballads*—clergyman who preaches before the bishop: "Dictum de omni").[8] Logic stands for becoming conscious of the procedure and not of premises.

Peirce's letter to Royce [1913]: [9] Schelling gets to the bottom of

---

by the estimates of others. He says, however, he can well understand why this was not done—referring, I suppose, to the greatly increased labor. He says at the close that if he could get a copy of this book, he would like to review it; and hopes that some time he may meet me personally." Woods and Peirce continued their correspondence, but they never met.

8   The lines occur in "Sir Macklin":
  " 'Then I shall demonstrate to you,
      According to the rules of Whately,
      That what is true of all, is true
      Of each, considered separately.' "
Cf. Costello, *A Philosophy of the Real and the Possible* (New York, 1954), p. 148.

9   So far, it has proved impossible to find the manuscript of this letter, which Max H. Fisch suggests may have been the one written by Peirce commenting on a presentation copy of Royce's *The Problem of Christianity*, and recalled by Royce in the first of his Berkeley Conference lectures (1914):

"He wrote me a very kind letter of acknowledgment which I deeply prize, and which showed that my so belated effort to understand and to expound the side of his opinions which was in question in this book, had received, despite his feebleness and his age, a reasonable and an unexpectedly careful, although necessarily a very summary attention and that my interpretation of him gained on the whole, his approval. I am grateful to the fortune which enabled me to exchange a last greeting with this so sadly solitary scholar, just before he passed away in the lonely dwelling place where his last years were spent"; quoted by J. H. Cotton, *Royce on the Human Self* (Cambridge, Massachusetts, 1954), p. 218. It would appear that Royce never got an answer to the letter he wrote to Peirce on March 4, 1914. See below, footnote 38, p. 124.

all science. Intuitions are expressions of instinct. If certain ultimate principles (instinctive) were not true, reasoning would fall. I have been surprised by sudden verifications. If we adopted hypotheses at random, we should probably never arrive anywhere.

Suggestion of hypotheses, *retroduction*— volitional, creative.	*Deduction*— absolute need of thought, applying signs: (1) Likenesses, non-analytic diagrams, icons. (2) Associations, names. (3) Symbols (general characters implied), tally marks, number.	*Induction*— similarity.	*Hypothesis*

Symbols involve thought proper. Symbols free. Nominalists miss symbols (general character). Parrots use symbols for they delight to deceive. Logicians have sought absolute certainty too much, and too much applications. Deductions relatively sterile. The small number of good hypotheses has given all sciences. Induction lies between the two.

Southard: On delusions.[10] Two things: (1) technique, (2) ideas about delusions. First neglected. False beliefs are interesting to

10   Southard's remarks approximate his paper "What Parts of the Brain Does Introspection Reach?" read at the December, 1913, meeting of the American Psychological Association and abstracted in the *Psychological Bulletin,* XI (February 15, 1914), 66–67. Cf. Southard, "On the Somatic Sources of Somatic Delusions," *Journal of Abnormal Psychology,* VII (December, 1912-January, 1913), 326–39; Southard and A. W. Stearns, "How Far Is the Environment Responsible for Delusions?" *Journal of Abnormal Psychology,* VIII (June-July, 1913), 117–30; Southard and A. S. Tepper, "The Possible Correlation Between Delusions and Cortex Lesions in General Paresis," *Journal of Abnormal Psychology,* VIII (October-November, 1913), 259–75; Southard, "The Mind Twist and Brain Spot Hypotheses in Psychopathology and Neuropathology," *Psychological Bulletin,* XI (April 15, 1914), 117–30. See F. P. Gay, *The Open Mind* (Chicago, 1938), pp. 233–37.

logicians. Wrote on delusions without noticing the problem directly. Avoid prejudice. Random collection of cases. [Delusions bear upon the] environment, self, and body—Wernicke [*Grundriss der Psychiatrie*, Vol. III].

Kraepelin: intellect, judgment; no localization in cortex. First like dream. General morbid change of whole cortex; affects whole personality. (Wundt.) False interpretation (process account), Stark remarks.[11]

Ziehen: [delusions are] not founded on sense but may modify it; six ways of development.

[Wernicke's] three-part division is workable: (1) somatopsychic, (2) allopsychic, and (3) autopsychic. Many errors in second. First is *clear*. Second probably not genetic. First caused by viscera or lesions en route to the brain. Second rare in paresis. Third was the most common. Autopsychic had frontal-lobe lesions. Lesions of frontal lobe with delusions of personality in paresis. Is then the self *motor?* And delusions, so intellectual, prove to be motor too? Examples of delusions. Some [patients] have good reasoning but inadequate data. Some, good memory but mal-ordering (metathesis). Cf. disorder of time in paresis, while space order is good.

Two groups of delusions: (a) phantastic (posterior association area), (b) pragmatic (anterior association area). Areas ripen later, different in tissue, more extensive in man.[12] (a) Paraphantastic beliefs, (b) parapragmatic beliefs. Not a contrast of content and process: (b) on expressive or motor side, (a) sensory; (b) cannot be cured by experience, (a) more absurd, less likely to lead to action. Introspection reaches (a) part, not (b).

---

[11] Costello wrote "Stark." Southard may have been referring to M. Allen Starr, the author of *Organic and Functional Nervous Diseases.*
[12] Costello sketched at this point a cross-section of the human brain, locating the centers of motor and sensory functions, the anterior association area of Flechsig, etc.

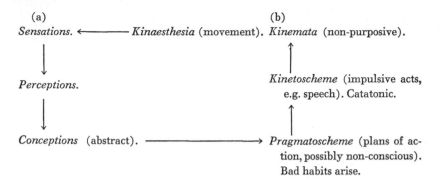

(a)   (b)
Sensations. ←——————— *Kinaesthesia* (movement). *Kinemata* (non-purposive).

Perceptions.   *Kinetoscheme* (impulsive acts,
                                                 e.g. speech). Catatonic.

Conceptions (abstract). ——————————→ *Pragmatoscheme* (plans of ac-
                                                 tion, possibly non-conscious).
                                                 Bad habits arise.

Royce: Method. New psychological analyses, many cases, autopsies, etc. Statistics, social in method. Fair samples. Machine-like
way of tabulating. (Reisner tabulated tombs automatically as possible.) Not "total impression," as with Wernicke. Incurability of
motors discussed. Case before James seminary; way of reacting was
important. Peirce's account of retroduction as instinctive acts, not
conscious of their methods.

[*Southard*]: Blindfold chess. Some said, "Could not tell"
[whether they had imagery(?)]. Best account.

Next: Troland or Woods or [? Southard on] fits.

October 28, 1913

৯ SUMMARY

Professor Royce brought before the seminary two letters written
by Charles S. Peirce (Harvard 1859, now in seventies). The first of
these letters, written to Dr. Woods in 1906, was of interest as insisting on the rather difficult logical doctrine that a principle of logic
can never itself be made a premise of any reasoning. The other

letter had just been received by Professor Royce, and reiterated
Peirce's belief that there is a mysterious harmony between the
mind of the scientist and the order of nature; for otherwise, supposing it were a mere matter of chance as to what hypotheses he
should devise, he would rarely hit upon any true and adequate explanations. The formation of hypotheses Peirce has called retroduction, and he contrasts this with deduction and induction. Deduction, though certain, is relatively sterile, and perhaps logicians have
attached too much importance to it. In connection with deduction
Peirce mentions his theory about the three kinds of signs, of which
one kind, symbols, involve an appeal to general characters or concepts, and hence if, as is probable, they are used by animals, they
indicate the presence of reasoning. But that to which we owe the
existence of science is not so much deductive thought, as it is the
discovery of a relatively small number of good hypotheses, and this
discovery seems due to a sort of instinct of the human mind which
brings it into harmony with the world about us.

After the reading of these letters, Professor Southard presented
some conclusions to which he had been led concerning delusions.
The method of the research into delusions consisted of an adequate
unbiased collection of cases, which collection was then reduced to
manageable proportions by as mechanical a tabulation as possible
and a selection therefrom of random examples. These typical cases
were then examined in greater detail, but with emphasis on statistics rather than intuitive "general impression."

Professor Southard explained and criticized certain opinions
about delusions held by various authors, Kraepelin, Ziehen, and
others, and also Wernicke's threefold classification of delusions
into those bearing upon the self, the body, and the environment.
Delusions directly explainable in terms of the environment are
found to be rare, while on the contrary those delusions about the
body, directly attributable to bodily conditions, are clearly marked
and frequent. Professor Southard gave examples of typical delusions, pointing out how some represented good reasoning from
inadequate data, others good data obtained from memory and

otherwise, but badly ordered (metathesis), etc. He himself found a twofold classification into *phantastic* or sensory delusions and *pragmatic* or motor delusions to be more adequate. This classification corresponds, furthermore, with data from autopsies, etc., if you suppose the after part of the brain to be chiefly sensory and the forward part predominantly motor. The motor side seems more or less unconscious in the sense of being beyond the range of ordinary introspection, but Professor Southard suggested a hypothetical scheme in which these motor processes should be shown to be equally as elaborate as the sensory differentiation into sensations, perceptions, and conceptions, the classes on the motor side being mere movements, definite impulsive acts, and thirdly, plans of action. But in any case, the importance of pragmatic delusions suggests that the intellect and judgment are motor rather than sensory.

I should like to add to this review of the last meeting, a couple of comments on Professor Southard's discussion. First, I do not know how much confidence Professor Southard reposes in his three sensory and three motor types of mental process, but such diagrams almost always seem to me rather deceiving than helpful, particularly if you try to draw further inferences from them; and in no subject is this more the case than in psychology. Take, for example, the division of introspective sensory content into sensations, percepts, and concepts. I have never been able to satisfy myself that I could obtain even a tolerably clear notion of what a concept was, introspectively, and I believe the term ordinarily stands for a diverse multitude of things.

This brings me to a second and perhaps more important point. Professor Southard expresses surprise that delusions, being such intellectual things, should turn out so frequently to be connected with the motor and not the sensory side. It may be a bias of mine, but I confess I should have been surprised had intellectual things turned out otherwise. Consider what is ordinarily called intellectual. The active side, for example, of *judgment* is evident enough. There is good reason to believe the great instrument of thought, *language,* is in its origin closely bound up with action and not with any arbitrary mental association of sensory content. The recent logician who has most thoroughly considered and analyzed the nature of *meaning*, namely Husserl (for example in the closing chapters of Volume II of the *Logische Untersuchungen*) finds, by arguments that seem to me at present to be quite overwhelming, that the identification of meaning with sensory context which is so frequently made, is in direct violation of the empirical facts, and does no honor to the psychology that carelessly admits it. Meaning, he says, must find its mental correlate in something of the nature of action, and this holds of the psychic character of concepts as much as it does of words. I might multiply examples. But perhaps I have said enough to show why I should have been surprised had intellectual things turned out otherwise than what Professor Southard finds them to be, namely predominantly motor rather than sensory.

November 4, 1913

ॐ NOTES

Southard continues: Vision has determined linguistic habits. Southard found in blindfold chess . . . the accuracy of one's knowledge was much greater than the accuracy of one's imagery.[13] Titchener's book reattracted Southard's attention to German work on imageless thought; where Titchener insists on sensation [*Lectures on the Experimental Psychology of the Thought-Processes*]. Older views of delusions laid stress on "fixed ideas."

Royce is of motor-speech type. Felt Hamlet was *before* him in delightful vividness, but found nothing but scraps on introspection.

Southard restated his view. Motor side elaborates before it acts. Consciousness may have no connection with cortex, or it may be

13 See Appendix A, below, p. 191. Cf. *A Philosophy of the Real and the Possible*, pp. 141–42. See also Gay, *The Open Mind*, pp. 297–99.

"smeared over" all cortex, or it may be localized (e.g., in areas— visual, etc.). Fore part of brain may have no consciousness; do not assign any until proved. If thought is wider than consciousness, there may be such. Conceptions are the chief problem for imageless thought. The "formula of thinking" may be found by the imagery, and may show where the source of the process was, but not how it is now.

Henderson: J. S. Haldane, *Mechanism, Life, and Personality* (experimental physiology); Hobhouse, *Development and Purpose.* An opinion in common: an escape for the vitalist. A non-antimechanistic vitalism. In no mechanistic account is there told the connection of stimulus and response. A "spontaneity," a "life principle" in every cell.

Southard: We ordinarily speak of the *unconscious.* Nobody wants to use the term. The *subconscious* has taken its place and [has been] discredited. The *co-conscious. Non-conscious* is better. James *-scious* only. Southard wishes to provide levels of non-conscious, "some levels of the non-conscious or so-called subconscious," as mentioned last time. The breaking up into levels Southard thinks an advance.

Henderson: Nobody has said anything on relation of stimulus and response which is both true and clear. Loeb is clear but obviously false.

Troland criticizes "spontaneity."

Henderson: Hobhouse twenty-five years ago thoroughgoing mechanist but other side has won. Evolution of mind.

Royce: Bergson's account of spontaneity. Same as James: considerations of consciousness involved. That you can't reduce to rule does not prove freedom. This act of choice never happened before —free in sense of unique. So Bergson; you need the whole enduring life. But ignorance is no proof in physical world. Southard spread James' view over all nature, and not consciousness only.

Henderson: Haldane on acidity of blood, etc. Variations in character of blood cause variation in respiration. How?

Troland: Trial and error best example of vitalism. But there is an analogy in trial-and-error way of giving off particles in radio-activity.

Henderson: Haldane criticizes severely vitalism (Driesch, etc.), and Hobhouse about Bergson the same. The *concept* of life is not mechanical.

Royce: Bergson's reference to memory as incapable of mechanical explanation—Peirce's hypothesis of tychism [in "The Doctrine of Necessity"].

Henderson: The more one knows of protoplasm the more complex the problem becomes. Dislikes theories of spontaneous mechanistic origin of life. In same way, a feeling has led men like Hobhouse, etc., to their new theory.

Woods: Wait a hundred thousand years.

Royce: Three things to consider: (1) Bergson, James, and Royce, study of consciousness—something hopeless to reduce to mechanism. (2) If the thing is too complex, this is ignorance. (3) You may find objects such that new uniformities are more and more mechanical in their type. Science can handle chance.

Henderson: Mechanism is only activity in a material system and hence obeys the fundamental laws of matter and energy—catalysis vs. freedom of will.

[*Southard*]: Seven hundred of a thousand insane show cortex lesions; two-thirds of the thousand *frontal,* with or without other [lesions]. Delusions very common in insanity. Second region of brain parietal (posterior association area). Normal brains (fifteen or twenty percent) showed often microscopic lesions.

Relativity, Troland, next meeting. *Troland:* relativity bibliography:[14]

1. Comstock, D. F., "The Principle of Relativity," *Science Conspectus,* II (December, 1911), 13–15; *ibid.* (January, 1912), 40–44.
2. Wetzel, R. A., "The New Relativity in Physics," *Science,* N.S. XXXVIII (October 3, 1913), 466–74.

[14] In the manuscript this bibliography comes at the beginning of the November 4 notes.

3. Comstock, D. F., "The Principle of Relativity," *Science*, N. S. XXXI (May 20, 1910), 767–72.
4. Carmichael, R. D., "On the Theory of Relativity: Mass, Force and Energy," *Physical Review*, 2nd Series, I (February, 1913), 161–78; "On the Theory of Relativity: Philosophical Aspects," *ibid.* (March, 1913), pp. 179–97.
5. Campbell, Norman, "The Common Sense of Relativity," *Philosophical Magazine*, 6th Series, XXI (April, 1911), 502–17.

November 4, 1913

&» SUMMARY

Some discussion of so-called imageless thought, by Professor Royce, opened the meeting; thought seems often to find its basis in tendencies to act rather than in any sensory imagery.

Professor Southard said what he had had in mind, in his discussion of pragmatic delusions at the previous meeting, was something he thought rather different. It was not an emphasis on action simply, but on an elaboration of the motor side before action; there were here found various levels of the non-conscious as regards its elaborateness, as if the motor mechanism had a certain constructive spontaneity.

The mention of the term "spontaneity" brought up what was to prove the central topic of the evening, namely vitalism versus mechanism. Professor Henderson called attention to two recent works, by Haldane, the physiologist, and by Hobhouse, which show a possible way of escape for the vitalist. There is, at the present time, no mechanical explanation which is both true and clear, of the relation between stimulus and response. The problems here are immensely complex.

Professor Royce called attention to three tenable points of view: (1) that of the mechanist, who says all failure to find the law of anything is due to our present ignorance of a complex subject-matter, and this will be done away with as we learn more about the subject; (2) that of the calculus of probabilities, which can handle uniformities of averages, even where the single event may seem due to the purest chance; (3) that view held by Bergson in his discussion of free will. Each life is unique, says the latter; from the nature of a process which at each stage has a certain duration and at each stage carries all its heredity along with it, no two moments are exactly alike; to see where it is coming out one must live it at full length. Memory is a typical example of a non-mechanical thing. Professor Royce did not treat of the possible conflicts of views (1) and (3), which seem to me almost certain, if they belong to the same temporal world.

Professor Southard closed the evening by a brief summary of some statistical results which tended to bear out his theory, mentioned at the last time, about a possible relation of the frontal lobes and pragmatic delusions.

My comment which follows is more elaborate than the summary given above, though I am going to deal with only one simple topic. I once outlined a hypothetical theory, concerning the relation of mechanical nature to organizations, and submitted it as part of a doctorate thesis at Harvard. This thesis is now gathering dust in the college library, and will doubtless continue to do so until some distant future age, when some curiosity hunter will disinter it, and discover to his surprise that all the original ideas of that future age have there been anticipated. I purpose here, however, forestalling that resurrection as regards a fraction of a paragraph. It is a very simple argument, and yet one about which I have felt some doubt, because if it were valid it would scarcely have been so frequently overlooked. Yet I give it to you for what it may be worth. It is commonly maintained there are two theories possible about organisms and no more: either the behavior of organisms is rigidly according to the laws of physics and chemistry, or else we have a mysterious new element entering to determine the behavior of the organic world, a vital force or spontaneity or whatever you choose to call it, so that the physical laws no longer strictly hold. But the mechanist then argues that you can get no proof that an organism is not subject to law, therefore vitalism is a gratuitous hypothesis. Nay more, it is false, for the further you go, the more do you find that organisms are rigidly subject to the ordinary laws of physical matter. Mr. Troland repeated what is a very typical remark, at the last time, when he said that the mere postulate that organisms are subject to the law of the conservation of energy suffices to prohibit that any new force can interfere, or any spontaneity break into the course of causality.

My thesis is simply that mechanism and vitalism, as above defined, do not exhaust the possibilities, and are not even inconsistent with one another. This is much less of a paradox than it may at first seem. Note I did not define mechanism as saying nowhere is there anything not of the nature of law, but as saying that physical laws hold rigidly in the organic world. Between these two statements there is a great logical difference, and that is what I wish to show. Suppose the law of conservation, as Mr. Troland argued, did predetermine completely the nature of an organism, so as to leave no loophole for vitalism; then it would have to predetermine still more. For it would be possible to predict all phenomena by the use of the principles of conservation; hence it would be possible to deduce, from the principle of conservation of energy alone, all the other laws of physics and chemistry, for example the law of the dissipation of energy, or the law of gravitation. I confess it seems to me a pretty bold undertaking. If you admit there are other laws not reducible to conservation of energy, then I point out the sharp distinction which is now evident between a law's being necessary for the determination of certain phenomena and its being sufficient.

Pure mathematics may possibly, as some logicians hold, be entirely deducible from a few postulates as to the relations of certain simple ideas. If so, for all mathematics these are necessary and sufficient. But if you leave pure ordinal mathematics and consider quantity, or again the ideas and relations one meets with in mechanics, sooner or later you must introduce certain new ideas and a few, perhaps a very few, postulates about the relation of these new ideas to the ideas of pure mathematics and to one another. Let it not for an instant be forgotten that the postulates of pure mathematics do not in this new realm in the least cease to be true, but they do cease to be sufficient. As we say, they are necessary but not sufficient.

It may well be that something of the like exists in the transition from the physical-chemical to the vital. One does not find in mechanics and physics that the laws of mathematics are broken. One finds them simply insufficient. New additional laws also are needed. Might not, in the transition from the physical to the vital, the old laws turn out to be valid but not sufficient? Suppose that physical phenomena are completely determined by physical-chemical laws; they are sufficient. Suppose that when you consider life phenomena, these laws are necessary but not sufficient; new laws enter. If so, now the vitalist can laugh at many of the proofs that organisms are subject to physical laws. There are (under these circumstances) peculiarly biological laws also, but suppose instead of these biological laws he introduces something which he calls the creation of novelty or spontaneity, how can you touch him by any proof that the physical laws hold good? All I wish to argue for is that no amount of proof that physical and chemical laws actually hold of organisms will of itself disprove either that there are special biological laws or the further thesis that there is a certain degree of spontaneity in a living being. The mechanist must prove not only that the physical-chemical laws are *necessary*, but also that they are *sufficient;* he must predict completely all the behavior of an organism from these laws alone and *prove that no other laws hold.* This thesis of mine is a comment, let it be noted, on the logic of the question; it shows the mechanist's task is a more subtle one than is sometimes appreciated, but my comment does not pretend to settle the further question of fact.

November 11, 1913

ও NOTES

Royce: Mill says there is no possibility of reducing all laws to one law. No a priori means of excluding from the world the unique, the spontaneous in this sense. This has a certain conflict with complete reduction to mechanical law.

Troland: On relativity. A new analysis of physical space and time and their relation. New light on time. Philosophers have thought of time as independent, in a way, of space, etc. Physical time and space are bound up, e.g., in measurement and motion, inseparably. Experimental verification. Philosophical and metaphysical. As a case of analysis of a scientific concept. *Method of hypothesis.* Elusiveness of conceptions of absolute time, magnitude, motion, etc.

1905, Albert Einstein (Swiss) [sic], following Lorentz. Implicit in Maxwell's electromagnetic laws. It is impossible to compare two physical lengths without considering time ("at the same time"). Means of establishing, and very meaning of, simultaneity. Simultaneity requires two events, separated in space. To prove that two events, A and B, are simultaneous, send a signal to or from a midpoint at same speed. Set two clocks at A and B. Speed at which light travels is independent of source.[15]

---

[15] Here Costello drew a diagram, copied from one that Troland put on the blackboard, demonstrating that to a stationary observer in system N, clocks A and B, within that system, started by a light impulse from point C midway between them, would appear to be in unison; but that to the same observer, clocks A' and B', started from midpoint C', in system M moving parallel to his system N, would appear not to be in unison. In the moving system, clock B', forward in the line of motion, would receive the light impulse later than clock A', which

(1) Impossible to detect the uniform translatory motion of any body (system) by observations made upon that body (system) alone. Both say the other is too large. Same holds for time. Sending and return of a flash of light would give a unit. (2) Velocity of light in free space is a constant, no matter what the conditions of observation are: $v = \dfrac{s}{t}$. Each claims other's unit of time is too long.

No proofs of earth's motion with reference to ether. Observer ought to be able to observe differences in velocity of light; Michelson-Morley experiments. The change in simultaneity and standards of distance and duration exactly counteracts the motion. Relativity asserts motion completely relative, no body is absolute. Out of harmony with ether hypothesis. Both observers are right. No absolute space-time-motion, in sense of absolute units. Duration, distance, simultaneity depend on each system. Either space and time are psychological subjectivities or mathematical relations. To the stationary observer the moving body contracts in line of motion. Is contraction apparent and not real? Dependence of velocity on source is impossible—optical behavior of binaries. Explanation of Michelson-Morley experiments, 1887.[16] Shortens in line of motion? —or velocity of light relative to earth? What do you mean by saying the contraction is only apparent? New conception of contraction: contraction from a point of view. Simply omits the absoluteness notion and a certain mathematical relation holds. Standards of measurement are a function of a point of view.

No objective metaphysical space and time, but only a relational system to put non-spatial elements in. Two observers ought to come to same results but don't. New concept of time abstract, complex;

---

would thus be ahead in its indication of time. To an observer in system M, however, the relative motion would seem attributable to the neighboring system, and it would be the clocks of system N that showed the discrepancy. Costello noted simply: "Light reaches A' before B'."

[16] A diagram in the manuscript shows two lines crossing at right angles, with a conventional representation of the sources of light and the mirrors used in the Michelson-Morley experiment.

includes change and simultaneity. Distance and uniform motion also needed to measure time. But does not uniform motion imply time? No, but change. In a static universe, time would be meaningless. (Bergson!!) Change is a succession of states like points in a line, replacement of one state by another. Time order is order of existence itself. Simultaneity involves multiplicity and causality. Clothesline theory of time is wrong (geometrical symbol). (More Bergson!) Hyper-metaphysics.

Discussion: Whole theory of relativity refers to uniform motions and not to accelerated motions. All so-called ether disturbances are independent of source.

Royce: Metrical vs. ordinal. Equality means simultaneous comparison of rigid bodies. No mathematical definition of equality of two lengths, except transformation of sets of points into sets of points. Superposition not valid in geometry. You fall back in geometry on another concept, an ordinal construction. You don't need an equality of lengths, but only optical alignment; distance which never involves simultaneity. Chronological concepts are ordinal. Simultaneity is better known to historians than to physicists.

[E. V.] Huntington, paper "A New Approach to the Theory of Relativity," *Philosophical Magazine,* [6th Series, XXIII (April, 1912), 494–513].

November 11, 1913

୫୭ SUMMARY

Professor Royce, at the beginning of the meeting, in discussing the logic of the mechanist's position, stated two propositions whose importance is sometimes overlooked: the first, one to which Mill called attention, that there seems to be no possibility of reducing all laws to one law; the second, that there is no a priori means of excluding from the world the unique and the individual—both of which propositions conflict, to a certain degree, with the attempt to reduce everything to mechanical law.

Mr. Troland then presented a discussion of the recent theory of relativity in physics.[17] In methods, it is an interesting case of the use of hypotheses, but Mr. Troland preferred to emphasize more especially its results, as showing the elusiveness of concepts of absolute time, magnitude, etc., and as revealing an intimate interrelation between the physical concepts of time and space.

The theory of relativity was, perhaps, implicit in Maxwell's electromagnetic laws, but was first explicitly formulated by Einstein in 1905, following out some suggestions of Lorentz. It is based on two postulates: (1) that it is impossible to detect the uniform translatory motion of any system by observations upon that system alone; (2) that the velocity of light, in free space, is a constant, and independent of the conditions of observation.

Mr. Troland illustrated, by an example in the form of a diagram, how two observers on bodies moving in reference to one another, would each, since each might well think himself at rest and the other in motion, be led to believe the other's units of time and distance too large. To any observer, a body moving with reference to him would seem to grow shorter in the line of motion. These deductions show why the Michelson-Morley experiments failed to reveal a motion of the earth relative to the ether of space, and they have led some physicists to reject the notion of an ether altogether. There is much experimental evidence, of various kinds, which would tend to support the relativity theory.

Mr. Troland was of the opinion that these results would force the philosopher to assert there was no such thing as metaphysically real objective space and time, and certainly the simple linear "clothesline" theory of time would have to be abandoned. Mr. Tro-

17 Headley writes: "Troland's report on the then relatively new doctrine of relativity included the information that the point of view developed by Einstein, at least in part, grew out of conversations over beer mugs from which the froth was blown in some inspiring way."

land then suggested in outline a theory about the nature of space and time which showed important affinities with the views of Kant and of Bergson.

In the discussion which followed, Professor Royce raised objections to the theory as presented, on the ground that it overemphasized the metrical concepts as against the ordinal, and overemphasized superposition as against those other tests of equality of distance which were defined by projective geometry.

I might add, on my own account, the following comment. Mr. Troland argued there can be no objective space, because it is logically impossible that of two bodies each should be shorter than the other. It is interesting to inquire whether this is true or not. When the Greeks first noticed the relativity of physical things, they were puzzled how a man could be both tall and short. Had they known about Kant and about the race of Esquimos, they might have argued: "It is absurd that a tall Esquimo should be a short man, and this proves the subjectivity of Esquimos." But this sort of relativity has, with familiarity, become a commonplace to us. Not so the new relativity of the relativity theory. Yet is the latter really more contradictory than the former? It is indeed startling to learn that a length is longer than another length from a certain point of view, and shorter than it from another point of view, but I do not see that it is contradictory or absurd. You may say the introduction of the term "point-of-view" indicates the introduction of something subjective. I answer I do not see that such is the case: replace Mr. Troland's observers by automatic machines, and the machines will record automatically the same results which Mr. Troland's observers take note of mentally.

I must insist, moreover, on a point which Professor Royce suggested at the last meeting, namely, the highly doubtful character, to begin with, of the concept of physical length. It is an empirical concept, suggested by experiences of rigid bodies. There are systems of geometry, perfectly self-consistent, which would apply only to a world where no body possessed a definable length. That two bodies are equal when they are together does not prove they are equal when apart, and this involves, in itself, no logical contradiction. Superposition is no adequate test of complete and permanent equality of lengths, as recent mathematicians have pointed out. Euclid, keener than many of his critics, used every device and circumlocution to avoid proofs by superposition. One *feels* that superposition is invalid, even apart from proof. I remember, as a high-school student, knowing nothing of the deeper theory of geometry, I had a sort of instinctive dislike of superposition as a test of equality, though I could not explain to the teacher why this was so.

To the relativity theory itself I have no right to offer objection, not having had the time to study its mathematical developments. Speaking subject to correction, I should be disposed to say in reply to Professor Royce's criticism of last time, that projective geometry enables us to define equalities of length, but not to create length itself, and, moreover, with the introduction of motion into the projective world, I suspect the relativity concepts would reappear. I confess the relativity theory has always attracted me through a certain appeal to the imagination, and I have found myself going off into semi-metaphysical speculations in a somewhat different direction from that taken by Mr. Troland. For example, if a wheel spins, and the rim shortens, what becomes of the mathematical value of π? Suppose you took a ride on a light wave: the earth would rush past you with the speed of light and thus flatten up like a pancake, and what would things look like then? Or again, when force is applied to a body already approaching the velocity of light, it increases in mass rather than in velocity. You thus get an equation of mass and energy. And I wondered if what seems to us length or mass, etc., might not appear, from some other point of view, as velocity, or heaven knows what, and here my imagination gave out entirely, and I leave it to the other members of the seminary to continue the research.

November 18, 1913

ᏃᏃ NOTES

Troland: Can an object be both circular and elliptical?

Royce: Geometry and mechanics of a people who could see and not touch, who saw things in mirrors, e.g., like the bowl of a spoon. Cf. Helmholtz's essays [*Vorträge und Reden,* Vol. II], first essay, "On the Foundations of Geometry" [Über den Ursprung und die Bedeutung der geometrischen Axiome"].[18] Occurrences which happen from a point of view, say of A, are nevertheless in themselves absolute. (The cat finds the cat in the mirror to be uninteresting.)

[On ordinal concepts]: Basis for most exact concepts of time. Historical or quasi-historical sciences. An event occurs or it does not occur. One uses the traces events have left, as in geology or archaeology, etc., as evidences. Progress in making and keeping records. Ordinal nature of records. Case of palace of Cnossus. Case of diplomatic correspondence which proved contemporaneousness of certain Assyrian and Egyptian kings. Geology of Connecticut Valley. Estimates of total length of geological period by salinity of sea water. We get over relativity by uniting points of view.

Troland: Relativity theory: no velocity greater than light, addition of velocities not simple.

[Next, Brogan. His references on judgment and value]: *Principia Mathematica,* I, 45–49, etc. Ethical theories of G. E. Moore, *Principia Ethica.*

---

[18] Cf. *A Philosophy of the Real and the Possible,* pp. 33–34.

November 18, 1913

ໆ SUMMARY

The discussion at the meeting chiefly concerned the relativity theory in physics, as presented at the previous meeting by Mr. Troland.

Professor Royce developed two propositions at some length. The first of these was that there might be a world whose geometry and mechanics might be very different from ours, a world comparable, for example, to the behavior of things as seen in a curved mirror like the bowl of a spoon. Though metrically there might seem to be great differences, ordinally the world in question would be in one-one correspondence with our world; so that the man in the mirror might not notice there was anything wrong, for his measuring rod would grow and decrease, or bend and twist, along with everything else, and he might think it was our world that was crooked. The second proposition was that the most exact or at least most absolute concepts of time are the ordinal concepts as they appear in the historical and quasi-historical sciences. Events occur, and this occurrence is absolute and irrevocable. As occurring, they fall into ordinal series. Examples were given where records revealed to archaeologists, geologists, etc., the order of sequence. As regards Mr. Troland's metaphysical theories, as presented at the previous meeting, Professor Royce held that the way to avoid relativity of points of view is not to get away from points of view altogether, but rather to get a point of view which includes them all.

Mr. Troland, in answer to a point incidentally raised, supplemented his previous discussion of relativity, by indicating how velocities could not be added directly—the velocity of light playing a part similar to an infinite velocity, so that twice the velocity of light was still the velocity of light.

In reply to Professor Royce's main contentions, he said the relativity problems did not arise in the examples Professor Royce adduced. Any occurrence on the earth, with objects not in rapid motion, would not reveal, empirically, the relativity difficulties. The case of change of solar time in a voyage over the Atlantic was not exactly analogous.

Professor Royce then introduced the case of a hypothetical visitor from Mars, who should compare earth-time with Mars-time, and thus by taking a more inclusive viewpoint at once reveal and at the same time overcome the relativity of viewpoints. Even by his success in arriving on the earth at all, he would, in so far, prove his calculations good.

Mr. Troland's reply to this, if I understood him correctly, might be illustrated in the following way. If a genuine contradiction is involved, we have not merely two points of view but two inconsistent points of view. It is not sufficient, in such a case, to get an inclusive point of view which shall perceive what were the other points of view, for it would itself thus contain still an unresolved inner contradiction. For example, if A pronounces picture X more beautiful than picture Y, and B on the contrary affirms Y is the more beautiful, you do not get a standard of beauty when you get an inclusive point of view which simply observes that A likes X and B likes Y. The only conclusion would so far be a skeptical one, such as that there is no disputing about tastes. Getting a more inclusive point of view may put you in position to observe a discrepancy, but it does not eliminate it. The relativity theory already, in thought if not in fact, occupies the position of the man from Mars; it observes a discrepancy which it cannot reconcile, and is therefore, for just this reason, led to deny objectivity to the physicist's space and time.

I have no comment to add to the discussion, except to repeat two points I mentioned at the last time. First, I said that the concept of spatial distance was already rather perplexing, before the relativity theory arose. If we conceive, for example, the material universe shrunk to the size of a pinhead, and ourselves and our measuring rods grown small in proportion, the sky would appear as far away as ever. The second point is the logical question, as to when we may be said to have an objective contradiction. Contradiction among propositions is clear enough; a proposition and its contradictory cannot both be true. But are the propositions "A is B from point of view K" and "A is not B from point of view L" contradictories? Obviously not. And yet this is the discrepancy which Mr. Troland calls a contradiction. Also, Mr. Troland showed a tendency to call an axis of reference a point of view and then to call a point of view subjective. But the central question is: as to when do we have a contradictory situation among objects which are not propositions? Is contradiction among objects itself relative to a system or a point of view? And lastly is not the object which is here threatened not any one of the physical exact concepts, but rather a popular idea of physical length, itself as vague as the older concept of causality?

November 25, 1913

ప~ NOTES

[*Royce*]: C. S. Peirce known as pragmatist, [and] as filling gap in Boolean calculus between Boole and Russell-Peano-Frege, especially Boole to Schröder. Postulate systems; began this though did not carry it far. Duality (De Morgan) generalized by Peirce until Schröder was able to state the general theorem of duality. Early stages of "logic of relatives" (cf. Baldwin's *Dictionary*): two forms due to Peirce, one yet undeveloped. Russell has attracted mathematicians' interest to it. Russell knows Peirce through Schröder. [Peirce] interested also in researches of Cantor. Peirce independently discovered one important theorem. Philosophical papers on logic, *Popular Science*, 1877–1878, began pragmatism. Other papers on cosmology (inductive speculation). Laws of physics are products of evolution. "The discovery of order is discovery of a problem." Disorder is "natural."

Nearly seventy-five years old. Only logician in *Who's Who*. Peirce's letter [to Woods]: from Milford, Pennsylvania, October 14 to November 19 [1913].[19] Received Woods' *Influence of Monarchs*. Criticizes Chapter 18. [Woods'] methods: unsurpassable use of inductive historiometry.[20]

Hypotheticals, contrary to fact, about individuals. Conditional: if A, then B. General "would-be." But if A presupposes an existential fact untrue, then the conditional proposition can do no more than establish a habit in the mind of the hearer. But if this habit could never be realized, it would be as nothing. The historian talks nonsense when he says, "If Napoleon had done differently he would have won Leipzig." When a man deliberates, he does say, "If I should do so and so." Essentially different because deliberator comes to a profitable conclusion. But historian knows already that antecedent is false. But if he could make it a maxim, a historian might be allowed to make an inductive generalization. *Meaning* equals *use for action*.

Reasoning and instinct. Instinct: animal's faculty of acting in an adaptive manner though its reasoning would not lead it to that con-

[19] Extracts from this letter have been published in Peirce's *Collected Papers*, VIII, 246-48. Woods had written to Peirce on October 10, reminding him of his willingness earlier to review *Heredity in Royalty* and asking him to compose a critical notice of *The Influence of Monarchs*. Peirce's long letter was a substitute for the desired review. Years later, writing to A. E. Wiggam, Woods said: "Royce [in his seminar] was always quoting Charles Peirce. I have no doubt he mentioned his name ten times as often as that of any other.

"One time I loaned him that long letter that Peirce wrote to me. Royce wished to read it to the seminar, and I was of course very pleased to have him do so, as you know I come out pretty well; and not only Southard was there to hear how fine I was, but also my old biochemical friend Lawrence Henderson, with whom I have had many a little scientific argument.

"I remember that when Royce read the portion in the early part, where Peirce refers to the soundness of my historiometry and the foolishness of my critics . . . Royce paused and put in these few words of his own: 'He certainly goes the limit,' and 'He is a hard man to suit.' "

[20] Peirce's phrase was, ". . . your mastery of the methods of inductive reasoning is unsurpassable."

clusion. Logic is based on instinct, the conscious part of the instinctive process, e.g., conflict and deliberation. Summary of his theory of probabilities: logician is not seeking perfect certainty, but the success like insurance. The instincts of animals that survive must be fairly true. Horse, dog, etc., have something like conscience. If one out of two hundred and fifty guesses is right, it is worth trying for. This is the only way. Don't despise "ideas." Dalton's atomic hypothesis. Merely entertaining a hypothesis is not yet induction, but worth while. [Peirce's] system of graphs.

Royce: All reason is instinct [and] is practical. Inductive is probability—all scientific reasoning. Deductive a special case, imperfect.

Brogan: Judgments of value. Are they true or false in the same sense as are physical facts? Realistic point of view. Meinong, Ehrenfels, Urban, etc., go into affective psychology and thus reach no good conclusion. Bad psychology mostly. Westermarck [*The Origin and Development of the Moral Ideas*], I, 17, gives history of theories of value. Not discussing moral facts as regards practical questions. B. Russell's account, *Principia Mathematica*, I, 45; essays [*The Problems of Philosophy*]: mind (subject) and objects. [Mind] has a sense, puts its objects in a certain order. Truth = R; [it] relates.[21] No truth without mind, but not dependent as to which one mind.

Value a confused term. Intrinsic value, intrinsic goodness. Good is unique and simple. Adjective *good* is indefinable; *meaning* not equivalent to *criteria*. Moore and Russell argue wrongly that because good seems simple it must be real. But Brogan assumes there is such an entity, Croce and Santayana hold judgments of value are not true or false, we choose for individual reasons. Fonsegrive says value is felt, not judged. Perry, Ehrenfels, Spinoza argue *good* means *we desire it*. Egocentric predicament.

Good and bad are independent of us as are round and square. Intrinsic value attaches only to human life and action. Affective side is part of this. So intrinsic values seem in a sense dependent on

---

[21]   See Whitehead and Russell, *Principia Mathematica*, I, 43.

consciousness, but not for their goodness or badness but only for their existence, just as Russell's judgments are.

Good, unlike truth, is unanalyzable. Contrast logic. Definition of concept and relation. Relation concepts. Even if good is a relation concept, it is not known by synthesis but only directly.

Aesthetic and extrinsic [values]. Aesthetic may be merely an expression of feeling or judgment of feeling and not of value. Beauty may refer to feelings of critic (Plato, Aristotle) or may be something *per se*. But latter is doubtful. Extrinsic values seem purely physical. There is possibly a value which is a relational product of this physical relation and the intrinsic relation of value, if the latter exists. Does not see how to unite physical and teleological or value [relations].

Progress: change to a greater intrinsic good. Best way to study value is through progress. Which possible modes, if chosen, would be better? (1) Terms of life. (2) One better than another. We then try to combine (1) [and] (2) into better possibility. This is place to begin study. Ethics has consisted of rules of formulation.

Royce: Induction in the proper sense. Perhaps use of hypothesis. Consensus of mankind is dangerous.

Brogan: But you must have a starting point.

Royce: Hypothesis goes on to something not common experience. How *test* different systems of ethics? Sharp difference between consensus of mankind and confirmations of science. Could you predict valuation judgments which have not yet been made? Can't eliminate philosophers, nor do you need to. Progress is a promising region.

Troland: Do conditions of ethics differ from psychology?

Brogan: Value arises in judgments.

Royce: Babbitt's theory of art—confusion of genres.

[Next]: Woods, "If" in history.

November 25, 1913
&~ SUMMARY

Professor Royce opened the meeting with some remarks about
the work of Charles S. Peirce, now living at Milford, Pennsylvania,
age seventy-five, the only man in *Who's Who* to give as his occu-
pation "logician." Professor Royce spoke of his contributions to
symbolic logic and also of his cosmological speculations.

He then read extracts from a long letter written by Peirce in in-
stallments from October 14 to November 19 of this year, addressed
to Dr. Woods. Among other opinions, Peirce expressed the following: Hypotheticals contrary to fact about individuals—if other than
maxims for conduct or plans for future activity; if, in short, they
can have no influence on action, but are mere speculations, as, for
example, what would have happened if Napoleon had done differently at Leipzig—are pure nonsense. As another topic, Peirce re-
turns to his theory about the basis of reasoning in instinct, and to his
idea that science would never have discovered so many good hypotheses had the discovery been solely due to chance.

Mr. Brogan next read a paper on the nature of judgments of
value. He said it was first necessary to lay down as a guiding idea
that values are objectively real, and that hence judgments about
them have an objective standard for truth and falsity, and are not
merely subjective preferences. As regards the nature of judgment
he accepted Mr. B. Russell's account, and for the nature of the good,
he accepted the proof by G. E. Moore that goodness cannot be
analyzed into something else, but is itself simple and unique,
though he did not deny that it might possibly stand in constant
functional relation to an unknown somewhat. Mr. Brogan considered aesthetic and instrumental values to be derived notions, but

value proper or goodness was intrinsic value, and, so far as he knew, was to be found nowhere else than in human life and action. He criticized all those theories which would reduce this intrinsic value to mere dependence on subjective desires and feelings. He thought that the conception of progress and study of examples of cases admitted to be cases of progress might furnish the best data for a more objective sort of inquiry into the nature of value.

Professor Royce, in criticism of the paper, said Mr. Brogan's incidental polemics against the philosophers were wasted energy, for the philosophers would persist unabashed by criticisms until the end of time. He said, further, that any attempt to test values by noting the fact that many people agreed as to whether something was valuable or not, was likely to result in false conclusions. We needed some method of hypothesis and prior prediction, putting the prediction to an empirical test later.

Mr. Brogan replied that there were great difficulties in the way of any such tests in the case of value, and so far as he could discover, there was no one infallible criterion of value.

By way of comment I might say, I don't see how Mr. Brogan is going to distinguish good data from bad, if value stands as unique and apart as he wishes to make it. Secondly, I don't think it does stand apart. Inquiries as to the setting in which value is found seem to me the only way to get hypotheses for testing. For example is there a relation between value and the *existence* of the value object, as Meinong supposes and Santayana denies? Or is there any truth in the hypothesis I once advanced that value is a sort of quality (*Gestaltsqualität*) which attaches to organizations, organizations being systems the chief characteristics of whose changes are found to be inwardly rather than externally determined? Such hypotheses confront many apparent exceptions. Can these exceptions be explained away, one by one? Such putting value into connection with other things seems to me the only way to approach the question at all objectively. Collecting and abstracting data of supposed experiences of value seems to me like proving the sky is a solid blue dome by getting many people to look at it.

December 2, 1913

ह NOTES

Discussion of Brogan.

[*Royce*]: Why does not Russell apply his theory of judgment structure to propositions? James, *The Will to Believe*—"The Moral Philosopher and the Moral Life"; Balfour, Appendix to *A Defence of Philosophic Doubt*. One who once is fully disposed to acknowledge that another finds something good, and needing my action to realize it—I give it a sort of objectivity. All things that anyone asks for furnish facts in my world. Perry adopted this.

Miss Webster: Used "objectivity" in different senses: usually contrasted with subjective, but neither defined. (1) Dualism: subjective, everything mental, vs. all physical objects (Descartes). (2) Bipolar nature of consciousness: all things known are objective. (3) Most interesting for value: mine and yours, subjective; common to all, objective. Professor Royce's definition of fitness treats of value with relation to objectivity in what sense? Common or universal? Brogan used objective value to mean intrinsic to human life and action, hence not wholly (1).

Mr. Brogan: "Objective" not a function of consciousness. Values dependent for existence on consciousness, but not for their value on consciousness, for any sort. Value is not equivalent to feeling of value.

Royce: If none of us desired, would there still be values?

Brogan: Yes! (!)

Troland: Nature of functional relations?

Brogan: Imaginary entities and their logical status.

Dr. Woods: Heredity and environment. Statistics on scientific attainment.[22] Cattell said [that according to] his study of scientific men in the United States, environment must be efficacious. But Massachusetts did not produce enough of highest scientific attainment. Woods replied, "probable error." Cattell admitted. Question not settled from American figures. Professor Pickering on elections to academies ["Foreign Associates of National Societies," *Popular Science Monthly*, 1908 and 1909].

Need a list of all scientific men: English (*Encyclopaedia Britannica*), German (*Meyers Konversations-Lexikon*), French (*La Grande Encyclopédie*). Fifteen hundred names [from each encyclopaedia], three or four hundred mentioned in all three. A: 300 or 400; B: 600? [mentioned in two]; C: about 2000 [mentioned only in one]. Greek and Italian Renaissance numerous in A. But otherwise [from] France, Germany, England. Rise in Germany and fall in France in nineteenth century. Not explicable by heredity in Germany.

Hefelbower: Since 1818–20, English students changed from France to Germany; Americans in 1830's.

[?*Woods*]: Recently Germany 71 to France 34; too much to Germany (etc.).

Royce vs. Woods: How define a class of scientific men? Is Kant a scientific man? Is Frazer?

Hefelbower vs. Brogan, etc.: 1845–90, Germany [led] in historians; later France. In mathematicians, etc., France has not lagged behind.

Royce: You need to get in [the] scientific type of mind: e.g. Berlin or St. Petersburg Academy. High grades of investigative learning, based on study of facts with scientific accuracy.

Discussion of "adjective" method:

Brogan: The man or what he did? "Eminence." Channing says

---

22 In substance this report was the same as Woods' paper "An Historiometric Study of Eminent Scientists," read at the December, 1913, meeting of the American Psychological Association and abstracted in the *Psychological Bulletin*, XI (February 15, 1914), 43–44. The reference to Cattell concerns the statistical studies published in *American Men of Science*, 2nd edition (1910).

"Hall of Fame is adventitious notoriety." Hall of Fame—forty-seven members, four times the number the population of Massachusetts calls for.

Royce suggests: (1) Take more or less inclusive classes; (2) take another equal class, history and philology and students of man—humanists. German definition of *Wissenschaft* here in question. Compare. What about practical men, engineers, explorers? Geographers? Along with politicians?

[Next]: Eliot, primitive religion and customs. Method? Hypothesis and truth. Notes.

December 2, 1913

ຂໍ SUMMARY

The opening discussion was concerning the sense in which values are objective, continuing the topic of the previous meeting. Professor Royce called attention to a theory which made the good semi-objective. The theory holds that if one is disposed to acknowledge that another finds something to be good, and if one lets this fact influence his conduct in the way of his trying to realize this good for the other person, then the good in question has a status not wholly subjective. This is the view of James in the essay "The Moral Philosopher and the Moral Life," of Balfour in the Appendix to his *Defence of Philosophic Doubt,* and also possibly the view of Professor Perry. Comment: I confess this theory seems to me to lend itself to caricature rather easily. If the baby wants to play in the fire, and if you act accordingly and put the baby in the fire, then you realize an objective good.

Miss Webster read a note inquiring the precise meaning of the term objective as used in the previous discussion. Did it mean: (1) physical objects as against mental in a Cartesian sense; or (2) everything thinkable as against the subject which thinks; or (3) common to all men, as against mine and yours?

In the discussion the third meaning was accepted. Mr. Brogan explained his theory of value further by saying values depended for their existence on particular consciousnesses, but differences of quality or degree in values were not dependent on any relation to consciousness.

The next subject for discussion was presented by Dr. Woods, who briefly summarized some statistics on scientific attainments in the exact and natural sciences. These statistics were drawn from data gathered from the English *Encyclopaedia Britannica*, from the French publication *La Grande Encyclopédie*, and in German, *Meyers Konversations-Lexikon*. He hoped, by comparison of the accounts given of scientific men from these diverse points of view, to get a fairly objective list of the recognized scientific men. He could compare the German with the English from the French standpoint, the German with the French from the English standpoint, etc., thus partly eliminating bias. From such a list it would be possible to study the variations of scientific activity in different countries; for example, the rise of German scientific activity.

Professor Royce recommended especially that a similar study be undertaken of the historians, philologists and students of man, in general the humanists, as comparison of the two lists, those of the natural scientists and of the humanists, might be very useful.

Comment on "objectivity": I should like to make a few remarks about the proper definition of "objectivity" for logical purposes, particularly so because my own criticisms of the papers by Mr. Troland and Mr. Brogan have undoubtedly been influenced by my presuppositions on this point and perhaps others' opinions by theirs.

There are various criteria by which we judge what is objective and what is not, but not all will do equally well as definitions of objectivity itself. For example, there is doubtless a difference in quality between being hit on the head by a brick and being "struck" by an idea, but this difference in vividness of presentation will not do as a definition of objectivity, unless you wish to say one half of the moon is an objective fact and the other half is nothing but an idea. Similar objections attach to the undoubtedly important criterion of richness and fullness of detail, which certainly often characterizes objective fact as against mental *schema*.

I shall limit consideration, therefore, to three criteria which have each been often given as the true definition of the objective, namely: (1) what is common to the experience of a number of persons; (2) what thwarts our efforts and our wishes and forces us to take account of itself; (3) what has a certain degree of systematic coherence.

First, the test of collective experience. As a general definition of objectivity it offers at least the following difficulties. If it means that that is objective which is agreed to be the actual common experience of a society of minds, then it presupposes the objective existence of such a society of minds, and this fact is not a matter of agreement, but a presupposition thereof. Furthermore, that on which even the majority of men really agree is rather seldom adequately true, and errors, such as the belief that the world was flat, have been at times almost universally maintained. If you say it is what men will come to believe in, in the long run, or what they ought to agree upon, then you certainly appeal to some other standard than agreement, something which will eventually compel agreement. If you say the agreement called for is not of everyone, but only agreement among a selected group of those competent to judge, the test of competence is again not agreement. To this it might be replied that the competent are men of a sort whose opinions in the past have subsequently been admitted by all, and hence the test is agreement. Not so, for the objectivity of the fact of this agreement is not itself an agreement, nor is the test of the objectivity of the resemblance of the competent of the present to those of the past necessarily an agreement of the sort here in question. My opinion, therefore, is that the competent agree because the facts they attain to are objective, and the facts are not objective because the competent agree.

Second, the test of opposition. This, I think, is if anything, more fundamental than the previous. You come to believe in the objective existence of your fellowman perhaps less because he agrees with you than because he differs from you in acts and opinions. The stone over which the savage stumbles takes on not only objectivity, but a living and malignant objectivity, for reasons of opposition and not of agreement. But the appearance of opposition and compulsion are not final tests of objectivity. Fixed ideas, erroneous beliefs, prejudices, we must admit have a sort of objective stubbornness, but it is often an objectivity of isolation, like ancient Egypt or China, which survives by resisting the importation of what might upset it.

Third, the test of coherence. This seems to me the most ultimate and the most useful as a definition. In a particular case, I may believe my fellowmen's opinions, often even as against the evidence of my own senses, because I have come to believe in the existence and the powers of my fellowmen. But I have come to believe in these because I have found them opposing as well as agreeing with me. And I believe they oppose or agree, because, unless those philosophers are right who say we have an a priori intuition of our fellows' existence, I first believe in the objectivity of the signs and evidences of their conduct and their expressions of opinion. But the reason for accepting these signs and evidences is that they take their place in some sort of coherent system.

Coherence, I admit, is an ambiguous term, so let me explain a little further. That sort of metaphysical coherence which says all things are constituted by their place in a system and all relations are internal and constitutive, may or may not be true, but it is in no wise here relevant. For in so far as all things are constituted by their relations, this offers no distinction between what is objective and what is not so. I require for the moment a less radical doctrine, one which all must admit, namely simply that things actually do have places in systems, whether constituted what they are thereby or not. Its place in such a system, spatial, temporal, causal, or whatever the system may be, determines the character of the entity's objectivity, though not, in so far forth, its reality. Had I need I might go on to distinguish this coherence of objects from the coherence of judgments used sometimes as a test of truth, or I might enter on the problem of the relation of the coherence of a mathematical system to the coherences of the physical world, but these would be other problems. But I believe the logician's final reason for saying A is more objective than B, is that A has place in a system which, in ways discovered and discoverable, is more varied than and of equal unity with any system in which you can place B. In so far, let it be remembered, I do not say the quality of A is or is not constituted by its place in that system, nor do I say A is more real than B, for these are further metaphysical problems.

Every hour we use the tests of being common to many minds, or of being resistant and stubborn as special tests of objectivity, but I believe the more ultimate test is coherence as above defined. This is why I objected to Mr. Troland that disagreements of different observers about lengths did not make space and time subjective so long as the relativity theory gave us a coherent system; and why I argued that Mr. Brogan could best prove values objective by connecting them in definite ways with other parts of an admittedly objective system.

December 9, 1913

ह NOTES

Royce: Is the proposition "There are values" a primitive proposition?

Brogan: In ethical systems, yes.

Discussion about ethical systems. Bentham.

Royce: Is proposition (above) self-evidence, or a dogma, or a postulate?

Brogan: Postulate, but a needed postulate.

[Discussion about] nature and function of definition. Russell, K. Schmidt; are their equations expressing a convention?

Eliot: Primitive religions. Problem: In comparative religion, in how far is it description and in how far interpretation? Can you treat religion as a form of social behavior, and what is behavior? Primitive mind's interpretation of its behavior is part of its behavior and interpretation of an early behavior.[23]

[23] Cf. Eliot's remarks in his Introduction to Charlotte Eliot's *Savonarola: A Dramatic Poem* (London, 1926), p. viii: "The rôle played by interpretation has often been neglected in the theory of knowledge. Even Kant, devoting a lifetime to the pursuit of categories, fixed only those which he believed, rightly or wrongly, to be permanent, and overlooked or neglected the fact that these are only the more stable of a vast system of categories in perpetual change. Some years ago, in a paper on *The Interpretation of Primitive Ritual*, I made an humble attempt to show that in many cases *no* interpretation of a rite could explain its origin. For the meaning of the series of acts is to the performers themselves an interpretation; the same ritual remaining practically unchanged may assume different meanings for different generations of performers; and the rite may even have originated before 'meaning' meant anything at all. The persons concerned may believe that the ritual is performed in order to induce a fall of rain; but this innocent belief throws no light on the genesis of their behaviour; and it is true even for the participants only in that if they became convinced that the rite had no effect upon the weather, they would probably, though with regret, cease the practice." Eliot added in a footnote, "The problem of interpretation was of great interest to that extraordinary philosopher Josiah Royce, for whose eye the paper in question was intended."

The paper, which led to discussions of "partial truth" (cf. Appendix A, below, p. 194), foreshadowed Eliot's critical emphasis on the modifying effect, upon the past, of successive interpretations. Thus he was to observe, "Every period of history is seen differently by every other period; the past is in perpetual flux, although only the past can be known. How usefully, therefore, may we supplement our direct knowledge of a period, by contrasting its view of a third, more remote period with our own views of this third period!" (Introduction to *Savonarola: A Dramatic Poem*, p. vii). The same premise underlies the idea of evolving tradition expressed in his "Tradition and the Individual Talent" (1919), that a new work of art modifies the relation of "existing monuments" to one another, so that "the past [is] altered by the present as much as the present is directed by the past"—on which he further commented, ". . . the difference between the present and the past is that the conscious present is an awareness of the past in a way and to an extent which the past's awareness of itself cannot show" (*Selected Essays 1917–1932*, New York, 1932, pp. 5, 6). Cf. Costello below, p. 87. Ethical implications of the same idea, in actions to "redeem" the past, are central to Eliot's later poetic work, especially "The Family Reunion," *Four Quartets*, "The Confidential Clerk," and "The Elder Statesman."

Based on Durkheim, *Les Règles de la méthode sociologique* [and Durkheim] "Représentations individuelles et représentations collectives," *Revue de Metaphysique et de Morale* [1898]; Lévy-Bruhl, *Les Fonctions mentales dans les sociétés inférieures.*

In Max Müller scientific definition is confused with philosophic interpretation. Same in recent times. Can any science [of] religion be arrived at? Protest against *evolution* of religion. No standard of evolution. Natural evolution can be considered from our point of view and with our values, not so social evolution. What is description? Religion is a practical though perhaps mistaken adaptation to environment (Tylor's "animism"; also A. Lang). Too much interpretation. Distinction between interpretation and a fact, a point of attention which has only one aspect or a definite aspect which places it in a system. When have I a fact? Progress in statement of problem in last ten or twenty years, as diagram shows (epistemological):

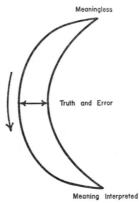

Why do we reject Tylor or Lang? Not because we prove them wrong. They bring forth good arguments, but we demand different presuppositions. Truth and falsity are relative to a level of interpretation. Lévy-Bruhl draws the line between the crude mentality of primitive [man] and his own [mentality] too sharply.[24]

[24] "M. Lévy-Bruhl . . . invents an elaborate 'prelogism' to account for the savage's identification of himself with his totem, where it is not certain that the savage, except so far as he had mental processes similar to our own, had any men-

Durkheim: [Relation of] group mind to individual mind analogous to relation of individual mind to body. He thinks the social
facts may be traced on their own account. Success chiefly as regards lower life. The social facts impose themselves on the individual. Any mode of action susceptible of exercising on the individual an external constraint is a social fact. [Durkheim's] rules: (1)
Consider social facts as things. (2) Set aside all preconceptions.
Contrast of concatenation of ideas and real laws of nature.

I. King [*The Development of Religion*]: Reaction [is a] fundamental psychic unit. Description of overt activities plus men's own
interpretation of them.

Statistical methods can be applied, e.g., to suicide. But is relaxa-
tion of religious restraint a cause of any given suicide? Must understand from within, otherwise behavior is mechanism. What is a
scientific description which is descriptive of the meaning of other
individuals? When does it go over into interpretation? The statement made on a certain level of truth [and] error is not the same
on another.

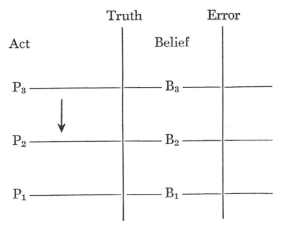

What is the fact at B_1 regarding B_2P_2? It may be B_2 about P_3. You

tal process at all" (Introduction to *Savonarola: A Dramatic Poem*, footnote
p. viii).

can interpret by intuitive sympathy with, or by making a series and studying places therein.

Up to a certain point the word "worship" is description; beyond that it it is doubtful interpretation. Miss Jane Harrison has studied evolution of ritual. But interpretation and metaphysics soon enter. "Purpose" is interpretation and not description. Frazer did another work: similarities and identities of races very remote; comparisons. Doubtful if he can arrive at what the purposes were. Durkheim: efficient cause and function, no purposes. Lévy-Bruhl really affirms really there is nothing to explain. Neither Harrison nor Frazer method is adequate. No causal relation, no definitions, no explanation seems adequate. Nothing but a chronicle. No explanation in terms of *need*. Transmutation of questions rather than a gaining of new facts.

Royce: No interpretation of meaning can be more than a hypothesis.

Eliot: Some theories truer than others.

Royce: Best method: At what level of meaning was a certain ritual?

Eliot: Interpretation which the individual makes is not made by the group and hence not the cause.

Brogan: Degrees of truth?

Eliot: Has a different meaning than what it has to us. Language may not be figurative, for he does not know it is figurative.

Royce: Child says, "I am a bird." (James: Obeyed and respected accordingly.)

Eliot: No judgment more than more or less true.

Royce: Every proposition has an infinity of implications—Peirce and De Morgan. One may be asserting a proposition without asserting all the inferences. A belief may be in an infinite number of respects related to others. Every proposition is true or false, but may be associated with false propositions and true, and [one] believes it all. Difficulty of analysis of such a complex belief.

Royce: On interpretations we make of one another. Are hypotheses regarding the intent of a sign [equivalent to] communication from another? Test: If I ask you a question, I can expect a certain kind of communication. Confirmation through answer; you can predict its type though not its details. When you interpret the social mind, you can't ask him questions, in general. Cf. vote about a government in England and [in] Germany.

Eliot: No interpretation helps another. Is there no essential distinction between a social statement in language which asks for interpretation and a something not intended as a sign? Difference between individuals' understanding and societies' understanding one another.

Troland: Psychological causes; only the introspective available (plus object?). Interpretation is bad description.

Royce: Mary Antin, *Promised Land;* Johnson, *Autobiography of a Slave.*[25]

Brogan: Is "exactly true" equal to "completely true"?

Royce: I make an infinite number of propositions at a time.

[Next]: Two reports. Sen Gupta, method in chronology.

December 9, 1913

ဗ္ SUMMARY

The meeting started with a discussion between Professor Royce and Mr. Brogan as to the status of the proposition "There are values": in what sense is it a primitive proposition, and is it self-evident, or a dogma, or a postulate?—the discussion going over into the further question as to the nature and function of a definition.

Mr. Eliot next followed with a paper on theories about comparative religion and in how far they were description and in how far interpretation. He quoted illustrations from various schools and periods: Max Müller, Tylor, Lang, Durkheim, Lévy-Bruhl, to show how uncertain were the facts or the very decision as to what would

[25] J. W. Johnson, *The Autobiography of an Ex-Colored Man* (Boston, 1912). (?)

constitute a fact, and how much there was of philosophic interpretation read into the data. Two lines of inquiry which he took for more detailed examination in this respect were Miss Jane Harrison's study of the evolution of ritual, and the comparisons instituted by Frazer between remote races. Mr. Eliot's conclusion was, on the whole, skeptical as to whether any conclusive results could be reached. The savage on a certain level interprets his ritual in a way probably not in accordance with the facts of its origin, but these interpretations become new facts and complicate the problem. Even modern scientific interpretations are subject to the same criticism, as really leading away from the facts. Interpretation is thus ever a new problem added to increase the difficulty of the old. Moreover, Mr. Eliot held that, epistemologically, what is sharply contrasted at one stage of development as the true and the false, takes on a different, more conciliatory, aspect at a more advanced stage, and, in short, there is no adequate truth short of the whole final truth. He thought the case of comparative religion especially good to bring this out, for here interpretation has succeeded interpretation, not because the older opinions were refuted, but because the point of view has changed.

Professor Royce, in commenting on the paper, said that an interpretation could, in everyday life, be tested by asking questions until mutual understanding was attained, but there were certainly difficulties involved in interpreting the social mind, especially that of primitive or departed races.

Mr. Eliot held another view of the nature of interpretation, and said no interpretation helps another. Interpretation adds to and thus falsifies the facts, and presents a new problem to disentangle. Interpretation is the other fellow's description.

The rest of the discussion turned on the notion of partial truth. Mr. Brogan wished to distinguish between exactly true and completely true. Professor Royce said what judgments one made would indeed be exactly true or false if they were simple, but they are always complex, so that one commits himself to an infinite number of propositions at once.

Comment: As regards the theory that there are degrees of truth
and that any judgment we might make is only partly true, I am
disposed to be critical, not to say skeptical. Certainly it involves
itself at once in a contradiction so sharp and so immediate that it
would be considered by the defenders of the opinion in question a
sufficient condemnation of any other theory except their own. If
all judgments are only more or less true, then the very judgments
by which the theory is arrived at are themselves only more or less
true. It may be retorted that my criticism is only more or less true,
and the supposed contradiction only more or less a contradiction. I
confess to a dissatisfaction which is not appeased by this dialectical
rejoinder, and in this theory as thus formulated I see no real escape
from endless relativity, since it defies even what seems to me direct
self-contradiction.

Professor Royce proposed to reconcile the theory with exact
logic, but with the way of that reconciliation I cannot agree, and I
should read the examples proposed in quite another way, not involving the notion of partial truth. One argument advanced by
Professor Royce was that every judgment is infinite in its real
meaning, for if I say "A horse is an animal," I stand logically committed to an infinity of propositions thereby implied, of the form
"The owner of a horse is the owner of an animal." I shall not here
inquire into the status of these, nor how immediately one can infer
that "A forty-horse power automobile is a forty-animal power automobile," or "A very small horse is a very small animal," or "A
horse-laugh is an animal laugh." But I do know this, that if I affirm
"A horse is an animal," and if the proposition is false, I am not
committed to any definite set of true propositions, and if it is true,
I am not committed to any false propositions implied thereby, for
there are none. This argument therefore seems to me irrelevant to
the notion of partial truth.

The second part of Professor Royce's argument was that in every
actual assertion I really affirm several propositions at once, some
of which may be false, so that my total assertion may be half or
two-thirds true, as the case may be. This way of taking the matter

is the sort of thing made prominent recently by Mr. Schiller, whose book on *Formal Logic* has been well characterized as a sympathetic appreciation of all known forms of fallacy. I grant that our meanings are often uncertain, and hence there is empirical ground for such a theory, but I should nevertheless avoid the contradictory notion of degrees of truth. There are various cases of possible ambiguity of meaning, which we may consider in turn.

First, a judgment may state a single proposition, but under conditions, presuppositions, or as intended only in a certain universe of discourse. We may not be able to state clearly what our presuppositions are, but if the judgment has meaning, it is wholly true or false, not half true. It is in some universe or other, and never in more than one, for if it were significant in two universes, it would be significant in the universe containing them both. If in this latter universe it were true only sometimes and false sometimes, it would be really a propositional function, and thus reduce to the case which follows.

Second, a judgment may state, let us say, that "All men are dishonest," and this may be held, with some show of justification, to be partly true, whereas "All men are triangles" is wholly or almost wholly false. But, as a matter of fact, it is a propositional function. So you have either stated "If X is a man, X is dishonest," and this is neither true nor false, or else it is asserted that, "For all possible values of X, if X is a man, X is dishonest," and this is definitely false if there is a single X to be found which is a man and yet is not dishonest.

Third comes the case suggested by Professor Royce's example drawn from the metaphysical problem of personal identity. It seems to me there is here no question of any half-truth due to the fact that I am committed to many propositions, part of which are false, but that [it is] the more likely it is neither true nor false, because I am not as yet committed to enough to make it significant at all. It fails not by overabundance but by coming short, if at all. In this I am in agreement with Mr. B. Russell. According to Russell, such a proposition as was discussed last time, the proposition

"Mr. Eliot read a paper" asserts one description of another description and is, in so far, neither true nor false. It is equivalent to the statement, "If X is what answers to the name Mr. Eliot, X read a paper, and there is only one such X." (Of course "a paper" is a description, and also needs some further expansion, but we may omit complications.) Here we have again a propositional function, this time dealing with a class of one. If there are two values which satisfy it, the propositional function is false for all values, and likewise if there are none it is false. But until you supply the value of X, you yourself are not committed to anything, either true or false. Mr. Russell thinks only immediate acquaintance can supply the X. There are difficulties to his opinion. But in any case there is no judgment here which is true, yet only partially true.

You may say I have simply substituted propositional function, neither true nor false, for judgment, half-true. At any rate, it has the advantage of removing the question from the psychological realm, and avoiding a blatant contradiction; and incidentally I have not been hereby led to admit that what any one judgment truly means is the sum total of all judgments, and I have said that ambiguity is a falling short and not the gateway to a realm which is beyond the true and the false.

One more remark I might add, and that is to call attention to the very important distinction, which Husserl and others have elaborated in some detail, between the *ambiguous* and the *indefinite*. If I say "Someone read a paper," my statement will remain true even though I later learn it was Mr. Eliot who read the paper. In the same way I might treat any ordinary judgment, including the judgment "Mr. Eliot read a paper." Such expressions, including most of ordinary language, may thus be taken as being definitely indefinite, without their being ambiguous. This way of taking the matter is, I think, in some ways preferable to Russell's extreme extension of the notion of propositional function, because enabling us to say statements are true or false, and a complete account would probably combine the two, but neither way of viewing the matter needs the notion of partial truth.

December 16, 1913

ટ≈ NOTES

Discussion about systems.

[Royce]: Peirce on fallacy of the liar. Distinguishes between what a proposition asserts and what it implies. It implies its own truth. It is false in what [it] implies and true in what it asserts.

Mr. Eliot said one needed to accept the theory of partial truth before one understood it.

Royce: Scott's reply about the author of *Waverley:* "No, I am not the author of *Waverley,* and if I were I should make you precisely the same answer." Weir Mitchell, asked by reporters about a notorious former patient: "You see, I always forget about my patients." Cf. assertions so made that it is implied he who makes them is not to be believed.

Eliot: (Note.) Interpretation is used in a sense which makes Royce's interpretation a rather special case. Cf. case of translation where verification is easy. But in more complex cases the question of identity becomes complex; e.g., the savage could not verify your interpretation of his thought. No sharp difference between interpretation of symbols and of facts. No sharp difference between expression and communication.

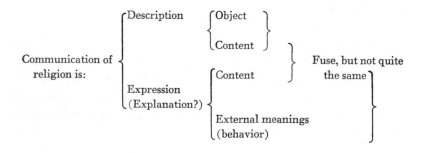

Description considered as expression cannot be handled on our level of truth and error the way we can handle expressions merely. When we have two interpreting each other, we have three points of view and great complexity. What is the status of a fact which includes a belief or a meaning?

Royce: Phenomenology of a religion is science of religious expressions, without paying *much* attention to the meaning. The Roman Catholic believer has a share in a certain "passive infallibility." People are fallible on the question as to on *what* decrees of the Pope are infallible. The believer carries out what the priest says. No one adequately understands, and they admit it.

Eliot: I see there are facts, but I am not sure what the facts are. What is he sincere about? *Behavior is the chief fact you have.*

Sen Gupta: [Note.] [26] Names: Pānini: date? Kātyāyana, first commentator. Patañjali, second commentator. Date of a philological work by Pānini: is it fifth [century] B.C., or seventh B.C., or tenth or eleventh B.C.? A special knotty problem. But there is close relation between him and the two others above. Patañjali's dates [have] fairly well been established: 150–100 B.C. Kātyāyana is about fourth century B.C. Language changed. Does not mention Sānkhya and Yoga, which were well known *circa* 315 B.C.

Pānini, change in language. New line of philosophic thought had arisen. Vedic grammarians arose between Pānini and Kātyāyana. No knowledge of Buddha, who died about 477 B.C. (477–481), born 557. Hence Pānini before 500 B.C. One hundred years not sufficient.

Not accepted. Sen Gupta himself has added a few references and details. Seventh-century hypothesis most probable. Sen Gupta's general method: Can you find one or two definite dates and the connections with the others?

---

[26] Headley remarks: "In addition to his powerful logical grip Professor Royce had a tenacious and comprehensive mind. Sen Gupta related to me his surprise, when he went to Professor Royce for advice regarding the methodological approach which he should use in his investigation of some rather obscure phase of ancient Hindu literature, to have Professor Royce evince intimate familiarity with the content of his study."

Brogan: Case of Homeric poems. Latest date but not further back?

Sen Gupta: Various independent sources.

Discussion about looking for facts to support a hypothesis.

Brogan: You see often only one theory.

Royce: Peirce on retroduction. Would explain the facts already known. The hypothesis that explains the already known facts is of little good.

Brogan: Subjective element. Date of *Iliad*. Considering agreements in text and disagreements in text.

Royce: "Argument from silence" is dangerous (in Sen Gupta's [note]). Case of Platonic writings.

[Next]: Hefelbower and Brogan on historical method; latter, interpretation of Aristotle and Plato, etc. January 6, 1914.

December 16, 1913

֍ SUMMARY

The meeting started with some discussion of points raised in the reports of previous meetings.

Professor Royce called attention to Peirce's treatment of the "fallacy of the liar," as when one says, "I am telling a lie" and stops with that. Peirce said this is true in what it asserts and false in what it implies, for it implies its own truth. Professor Royce further called attention to the problem of the truth of Scott's reply when asked if he was the author of *Waverley:* "No, I am not the author of *Waverley,* and if I were, I should make you precisely the same answer."

Mr. Eliot added some remarks in support of the theory that all judgments we have power to make are only partly true. I am not sure I caught the point, but I understood him to assert that a judgment can be partly true without being partly false, and further, that in order to understand the theory of partial truth you first have to believe in it.

Mr. Eliot then presented a note on his use of the term "interpretation" and the difficulties to which it pointed. The great question is as to what is the status of a supposed fact which includes as part of itself a belief or a meaning? How can we be sure we are correctly interpreting the mental life of a savage when the savage could not verify our interpretation if we could present it to him, because he could not understand it? Professor Royce's "interpretations" are interchanges of ideas by people more or less on a level, but the case is not so simple when the interplay is between vastly different levels of culture.

Professor Royce, in comment, brought forward the case of the Roman Catholic, who explicitly declares he believes without understanding. One thing we can do in such cases, and that is to study the phenomenology of religion, considering the various types of religious expression without much attention to their deeper meaning.

Mr. Eliot replied that behavior was indeed the chief fact you have, but behavior is mere mechanism unless you perceive it has some sort of meaning—and then the question is, What is that meaning?

Mr. Sen Gupta then read a paper on certain methods of work in investigating cases of Hindu chronology. The illustration used was that of fixing the date of Pāṇini, who wrote an early philological work. The dates of two of his commentators were first fixed, and by the internal differences of language between these and Pāṇini, his apparent ignorance of Buddhism, etc., his date was fixed as at least before 500 B.C. The general method was to find one or two definite dates and the probable relations of these to the conjectural dates, considerable weight being given to convergence of independent sources of information.

In the discussion which followed, Professor Royce pointed out the dangers of the argument from his silence as regards a certain topic, on the part of an author, to his ignorance of that topic. Also the danger of hypotheses which merely seem to explain the known facts without leading to the discovery of new ones.

Mr. Brogan called attention to the similar problem of the Homeric poems and insisted on the subjective element in all such inquiries.

Comment: I should like to add a few rather scattered remarks: I. I should like to ask if in comparing the language of two authors in determining their relative dates, one should give the same value to changes in the use of words and to changes in grammar? Mr. Sen Gupta did not make clear this point, mentioning grammar changes along with word changes. We all know how rapidly words shift their meanings, but grammar seems the very structure and skeleton of the language itself, and highly immune from innovation.

II. A hypothesis which is of the nature of a reconstruction of an individual past event seems to me different markedly from a hypothesis which leads to a deductive theory of a generalized nature. The hypothesis of the detective who reconstructs the scene of a crime seems to be formed on different principles and differently verified from, let us say, the relativity hypothesis in physics. Has anyone discussed in detail these differences existing between the *historical* hypotheses and the *theoretical* hypotheses?

III. The methods of scholarship seem to have been much neglected as compared with the methods of science. Yet in these fields the advance in precision has been in comparatively recent times as great as that in any field of science, with the possible exception of mathematics. The making of an edition, even the mere correcting of clerical errors in a manuscript of a classical author, demands a very high grade of ability and methods of considerable delicacy. One does not correct errors by a guess as to what would read best; one must be able to tell why the error was committed. Even mere textual criticism thus becomes a historical science, and one which makes great demands in the way both of originality and accuracy. The same is true of the higher criticism, although here unfortunately it is just those questions which are most controversial, such as the authorship of the Homeric poems, which attract the most public attention, and lead the outsider to overlook the really solid accomplishments. In philology proper, similar standards are now demanded, as for example in Murray's great *Oxford Dictionary*. All this sort of work has received too little attention from logicians.

IV. I should like further enlightenment on Professor Royce's views about interpretation. Professor Hocking of Yale, in his recent talk here, criticized Professor Royce's views in the following way. Professor Royce says an interpretation itself needs a further interpretation and so on. Each interpretation is thus essentially transitory. If so, then *art* is not an interpretation of nature and of human life, for each artist, each poet, intends his work to endure and if it is good art it does endure. I ask, would Professor Royce consider this a fair interpretation of what he means by interpretation? And furthermore, is a work of art essentially a changeless thing, as so many assert? Does not each generation have to reinterpret the masterpieces for itself? What is there, then, which remains absolutely identical in the work of art, beyond the substance of the paint or the printer's ink? I simply raise the questions, for I am very doubtful on these points.

January 6, 1914

౭ఌ NOTES

[*Royce*]: Professor Henderson sends an article on comparative science, relation between organism and environment.[27] A new order among chemical properties, a dynamic order, evolutionary.

[27] L. J. Henderson, "The Functions of an Environment," read before the American Society of Naturalists, December 31, 1913, and published in *Science*, N.S. XXXIX (April 10, 1914), 524–27.

The properties are not evenly [distributed] among the elements nor in periodic-law form merely. A few elements, hydrogen, oxygen, and carbon, have a large number of extreme properties. Thence results follow which could not otherwise occur. Maximal stability and maximal complexity on the surface of a planet, and maximal complexity, durability, and activity of systems. Purely physical-chemical measurable considerations. But for biology result is that the actual environment is the fittest possible abode of life, given the present elements. Water, carbonic acid, and hydrogen, oxygen, carbon are unique. Any physico-chemical system (aggregate of matter at a position, form, and size in space) is defined abstractly by the phase rule, and will manifest activity (energetics). It is a mechanism, an active system. It has at least some durability. Hence fitness for mechanism can be studied apart from life. [Water makes possible the] greatest components, phases, concentration; [extreme] temperatures, pressures [are] not consistent with durability. Hydrogen, oxygen, carbon are best means for storing and distributing energy. Water restricts temperatures and many elements are soluble. CO_2 preserves same alkalinity of ocean, etc. Fittest for durable mechanism. The fitness of the organism is much less precise and more local. Because life must operate this mechanism it is conditioned. The special characteristic of inorganic is fittest for those general characteristics of organic which the general characteristics of inorganic impose on it.

Troland: The mechanist has always held matter favors life.

Royce: This is not mechanism as such.

Troland: Coincidence of maxima. He did not bring this out in his book.

Royce: Why should vapor tension and solubility and specific heat go together and be all an aid to mechanism?

Troland: Explained by an electrical theory, possibly, hence not independent.

Brogan: "If" in history is same thing.

Royce: Peirce said an "if" about individuals was bad—not universal hypotheticals. Newton.

Brogan: No, it describes a world different from this and is not Newton's.

Hefelbower: [Note.] A principle and a particular problem. It often happens that later importance of one principle leads it to dwarf, in interpreting previous ages, what was then really important. Genetic method, too extreme application, evolution, continuity, each age carrying on just that which preceded, nothing of importance dropping out. We study backward, say from Plato or from Kant, etc. Deistic movement is more or less associated with philosophic empiricism. English deism is interpreted through French eyes and not as it was. Genetic method considers only that which later became historically significant. Is the series a mathematical continuum? One-dimensional series in so far. But there were other contemporaneous branches, not one-dimensional.

Discussion of evolutionary trees.

Eliot: What is your criterion of importance? How can we say something was important in a past age if nothing followed from it?

[*Hefelbower*]: Question not raised.

Royce: Many lines, not one. Look for the neglected contemporaries. Case of Fichte. Leibniz, *New Essays.*

Eliot: There is no importance *at one time* historically.

Royce: Two cases tonight of evolutionary theories.

January 6, 1914

ᔢ SUMMARY [28]

Professor Royce began by reading Professor Henderson's most recent restatement of his views about "fitness," the substance being

---

[28] A marginal note pencilled at the beginning of this summary cites Conrad Hermann's *Die Sprachwissenschaft* and Ernst Elster's *Prinzipien der Literaturwissenschaft.* Possibly it relates to the latter part of the December 16 summary, above, pp. 86–87, item III.

the same as that of his statements before this seminary earlier in the year, but the form of statement altered to avoid the misunderstandings that had arisen. The theory claims to have discovered a new order among chemical properties, a dynamic order. Properties are not evenly distributed among the elements nor distributed merely according to the periodic law. A few elements, hydrogen, oxygen, carbon, have a large number of extreme properties, and these elements, it also so happens, are the common elements on the surface of a planet. The properties which hydrogen, oxygen, carbon and certain of their compounds such as water and carbon dioxide possess in a maximal degree, are measurable physical and chemical properties; and the coincidence of these maxima in these few elements is, therefore, capable of proof. It can further be shown that the possession by such common elements of such extreme properties leads to maximal stability and maximal complexity on the surface of a planet, and to the maximal number, complexity, durability, and activity of the physico-chemical systems found there. If we call such active systems mechanisms, the present environment is the fittest of any composed of the present known elements for the existence of durable mechanisms. And since life must operate through such mechanisms, it is true that, from a strictly physical-chemical standpoint, the present environment is the fittest possible for living organisms. This definition of the fitness of the environment is more general and more exact than any definition we can give of the fitness of the organisms for their environment. Conclusion: The special characteristics of the inorganic are the fittest possible for those general characters which the general characteristics of the inorganic impose upon the organic.

Mr. Troland, by way of comment on the paper, said that the mechanist had always held matter was sufficient to produce life. Professor Royce replied to this, that it was not determinism as such which was here in question, but certain peculiar properties which might or might not be possessed by a deterministic world. Mr. Troland added the further comment that Professor Henderson had not, in his earlier writings, sufficiently emphasized that it was not the existence of maxima that he had discovered, but this peculiar coincidence of maxima in the common elements. This coincidence was the gist of it all, and this itself might soon be explained in terms of deductions from some general electrical theory of matter.

Mr. Brogan objected that Professor Henderson was comparing what is with what might be, and this was not scientific but speculative. Professor Royce replied that, for example, Newton's laws stated something ideal. Mr. Brogan said that Newton's laws were abstract products of analysis of what exists, and they would apply to the world as it is if we had power to calculate all the complex of factors involved. But Professor Henderson's hypothetical cases are of what would happen if certain concrete elements were omitted, leaving the others unchanged. How do you know that simple omission is possible, the other elements being unchanged? The objections of Mr. Troland and Mr. Brogan thus both took the form of suspecting a greater interdependence among physical properties than is now known to exist. Professor Royce said what Professor Henderson had done was to indicate some remarkable characteristics of data already known to us, and these characteristics were facts, whether they admitted of deeper explanation or not.

The seminary then turned to the consideration of historical methods. Mr. Hefelbower spoke briefly on a certain tendency towards fallacy in historical investigations, which tendency arises owing to an overemphasis on the genetic method and on tracing single chains of evolution. The tendency was to see in an age not what it itself was, but only what it contained of germs which were later to develop. One thus came to follow exclusively a single thread of development, even where the actual history had many strands. A typical example of such is in our present-day treatment of the deistic movement in England.

Mr. Eliot wished to know by what criterion of importance Mr. Hefelbower was measuring historical events. The reply was that this question was not raised. Mr. Hefelbower held that it was sufficient to notice what it was the people of a given period thought important. Professor Royce mentioned other examples of Mr. Hefelbower's thesis, among them the case of Fichte's later writings, whose influence did not arise until very recently, although they were the true Fichte. Professor Royce said the methodological principle involved was that of looking for the neglected contemporaries of striking events, for in those contemporaries were often contained the forces which really molded both their own and subsequent periods.

Comment: I understood Mr. Hefelbower, in his own presentation, to be interested in something which the subsequent discussion did not bring out. The later discussion insisted on a *completer* use of the genetic method, a use which should note that history contained many strands, and that the neglected contemporary of one age might be the moving force of the next. But Mr. Hefelbower's first thesis seemed to be a general criticism of the genetic method as such, a doubt whether it ever furnished an account in every way adequate. Each age has an individuality of its own which is not simply bequeathed *in toto* to the next; the movement of evolution has its losses as well as its gains. To revive the atmosphere, the tang, the color, of a particular age, we must not fail to call attention to aspects which perhaps were peculiar to that age, neither important in any previous generation nor destined to have any marked direct results on subsequent times. The genetic method tries to explain one age in terms of the next, it passes you on endlessly from one to another with no resting place; whereas, for the people of a given epoch, the fact that they were destined to be good ancestors was not what constituted their life as they experienced it. This seemed to me, as I heard Mr. Hefelbower's first account, to be what he had in mind, but the later discussion took quite a different turn.

January 13, 1914

৯৯ NOTES

[*?Royce*]: Methodology is an empirical science. All you can get
are surveys of work in general fields. You can get scientific general-
izations.

Royce: [Assignment.] Nature and limits of explanation. Contrast with description. How do you explain? You perhaps reduce to
more general principles and unify a larger variety. Classification is
description, so is statistics—explanations are not yet in question.
Would Dr. Woods' germ-plasm hypothesis about the course of history be an explanation? Is the difference one of degree? Is description a shortcoming? Kelvin regretted his failure to reach an
"explanation" of electricity. Was this a mistake? Is explanation beyond human power? Kelvin was not seeking a metaphysical explanation. What did he want? There have been deliberate efforts
to banish the word "explanation": Mach, Karl Pearson, Wundt,
Kirchhoff (introduction to lectures on mechanics). Describe simply
and fully the movements which take place. "Force" is of value only
if it enables us to describe. Questions of vitalism, fitness, etc., raise
the question in new shapes. The describers are somewhat in the
background. A descriptive hypothesis about possible experience is
an explanation? Three things which are called explanations: (1)
Answer to question "Why?"—teleological. Non-scientific? (2) A
description is of phenomena, an explanation shows what is really
there. Appearance vs. reality. Degrees of explanation. Appearance
of space objects vs. geometrical account. Kelvin regretted this, probably? (3) Wundt's view, and Enriques on the *Problems of Science.*
The doctrine of the importance of the associations of sensory experience. Relative difference: explanation is characterized by syn-

thesis, description by analysis. Explanation takes account of large connections; description, of a multitude of details. Definition is best which enables you to deduce more theorems. You get explanation of the parts in terms of a larger whole you unify. (First meeting after midyear, united session; ten-minute note from each. Note on explanation: define. Importance. False ideal? Vague?) Cf. . . . Arthur Gordon Webster [address before the Physics Section of the American Association for the Advancement of Science], Atlanta, in December [1913]: "The Methods of the Physical Sciences. To What Are They Applicable?" *Science*, [N.S. XXXIX] (January 9, 1914), [42–51].

Henderson: [29] Mechanistic view of life. Mechanism is philosophically employed to mean a blind and necessary connection. Since Aristotle the teleological has been imposed upon the mechanistic. One does not deny the utility of mechanism. There are teleological accounts which seem to be preferable, e.g., in solving a problem of calculus or in noting the behavior of W. Wilson. The present-day mechanistic account of these is of small worth. Might it later be possible to explain these [as] ultimately mechanical? Pass this by, because doubtful and metaphysical. Mechanism does not account for the *existence* of matter and energy. Du Bois-Reymond's Seven World-Riddles are still riddles. The question appears to be: To what extent and in what respects is mechanistic explanation likely to suffice? Henderson believes natural science finds mechanism sufficient, perhaps even psychology. Qualification: existence of life is a riddle at present. Difficulty of imagining origin of life is enormous for the chemist. The strong argument for the mechanistic explanation is that it is the only way known to physical science: matter and energy. (In painting a picture or fighting a battle the very highest elements are not mechanistically describable.) Second argument: no way of conceiving of the diverting [of] a physical-chemical process without expenditure of energy. Directive force

---

[29] Henderson's *The Order of Nature: An Essay* (Cambridge, Massachusetts, 1917) reformulated the conclusions of this sketch and of his article in *Science*, N.S. XXXIX, 524–27.

may be extremely small. In catalysis this is true. No sound explanation how you could divert a stream of causality without some energy. Thirty years ago in France, efforts of mathematical physicists failed. "Freedom of will" vs. conservation of energy. Vital force, as a form of energy, and vital substances are gone.

Behavior is purposive, however. Function and response do involve purpose. Hobhouse comes nearest to stating vitalism. Notable because not in defense of a thesis—a result of a progress of twenty years. [*Development and Purpose*], p. 325. Conclusion: If you consider purpose in human action: a unique want is brought into connection with a unique experience, or there is a new situation. Henderson in doubt; this better than Driesch and Bergson. Define mechanism as previously defined: an aggregate of matter occupying a portion of space is a system. Systems have duration and activities (energy acting through systems). A mechanism is any active system. Can use this in physics, chemistry, physiology. "Natural selection" is a mechanistic explanation of the teleological. You can recognize the teleological in mechanism itself, as in the discussion of fitness, a "maximum"; this is a teleological question. The number, variety, complexity, durability are a maximum. Is it not right to assume the same thing for organic teleology? It is there from the beginning; it is simply there from the beginning. Otherwise it is simply a mechanistic problem. If anything happens, it happens in accordance with the laws of matter and energy.

Royce: Parallelism of teleological and mechanical. Inductive result.

Troland: Psycho-physical parallelism the only possibility. Ultimately mind-stuff theory.

Brogan: Modern efforts anti-parallelistic.

Discussion of psychical causation.

[*Royce*]: Peirce's objective chance.

January 13, 1914

?❧ SUMMARY

Professor Royce set as a topic for discussion immediately after the midyears the question of the nature and limits of explanation. For example, does it differ from description merely by being more general? What was it that Kelvin felt the need of, when he regretted that he had failed to reach an explanation of electricity? Was this a mistake on Kelvin's part, and should the word "explanation" be banished from the scientific vocabulary? Mach, Pearson, Kirchhoff, and others have held that the one task of science is to give a simple and accurate description of what happens, without any attempt at a deeper explanation. But if one even brings in possible experiences, as against actual ones, is one not going beyond mere description? The mere describers are less prominent in scientific discussion to-day than they were a few years back. But explanation remains an indefinite term. (1) Does it mean an answer to the question, Why? —i.e., is it teleological? (2) Or does description treat of phenomena, of appearance; and explanation penetrate deeper into what is really there? (3) Or is the difference this, that description is analytic and explanation synthetic; that description is detailed, and explanation an account of the larger connections? This whole question will be the topic for February 10.

Professor Henderson then presented a first sketch of some ideas about mechanism and teleology, which he hoped to work up later into a paper. The value of the mechanistic account of things is widely admitted, but there are cases, such as in solving a problem or in observing human conduct, which are certainly more easily explained teleologically. This is not to say they do not have a mechanistic explanation. Of course, ultimate questions, such as why there exist matter and energy at all; perhaps, also, what is the origin of

life, are questions which mechanism cannot solve. But all natural
science, up to and possibly including psychology, finds the mechanistic explanation sufficient. In the first place, it is the only way
known to physical science; in the second place, there is no way of
conceiving the diverting of a physical-chemical process without expenditure of energy, even though the directive force be extremely
small.

While thus admitting the universal scientific application of
mechanism, the fact remains that organisms are also teleological:
behavior, function and response have a purposive character. Yet no
vitalistic account seems tenable. Hobhouse succeeds best when he
says that, in the case where a unique want is brought into connection with a unique experience, such a new situation cannot be
mechanistically predetermined. Professor Henderson protested he
could not understand the vitalists, even as Hobhouse states their
case. But nevertheless it did seem to him that the teleological could
be found not merely in the organic, but, as the case of "fitness"
showed, in the inorganic as well; as if mechanism and teleology ran
parallel from the very first.

In the discussion which followed, Mr. Troland said he believed
psycho-physical parallelism the only possibility for science, but
some sort of panpsychist theory to be the metaphysical explanation.
Mr. Brogan said present tendencies were anti-parallelistic. Dr. Costello said Professor Henderson's argument that it required energy
to divert a physical-chemical process seemed, as thus stated, to involve a fallacy of begging the question, since it presupposed the
sufficiency of the mechanistic explanation before the notion of diverting had any precise meaning, thus putting into the premise
what was to be drawn out in the conclusion. Professor Henderson
said the premise was nevertheless true, and anyone who doubted it
was not worthy of further consideration. Neither this discussion nor
one about psychical causation seemed to get anywhere. At the close
of the meeting Professor Royce called attention to Peirce's views
about objective chance, and the possibility that all physical laws
were only approximate.

Comment: My own attitude towards the problem raised by Professor Henderson has always been one of trying to find out what the problem was and not one of settling it. It is generally hopeless to enter on any debate about, let us say, the freedom of the will, because of the difficulty of getting the problem stated. The older notions of causality have suffered, as is well known, a similar criticism. I shall assume that causality in its vague forms has been effectively criticized, and that the only tenable form of scientific determinism is that of mathematically statable laws and the deductions which follow from them. If so, we can consider the question from the standpoint of the logic of deductive systems, for at least the logic must be cleared up before the question of fact can be raised.

First let me interpose a remark about Peirce's notion that physical laws are only approximate, as mentioned by Professor Royce. One who held this might be the purest physical determinist, and what he would mean would then be that our brief statements of laws are always too simple. Otherwise the conception of Peirce's is more like the old Greek notion that matter is resistant to form than it is like modern scientific notions: it conceives of certain norms as only approximately realized. At any rate Peirce's view is not widely held, and I therefore pass on to another topic.

That topic is one which I brought up in a previous meeting. It is, namely, that the mere proof that any given law or set of laws holds rigidly of certain phenomena would not itself prove the phenomena in question were completely determined by these laws. This is a purely logical observation. Given a set of postulates for a deductive system, there is a set of theorems for the deduction of which these postulates are necessary and sufficient. But examples can be drawn from mathematics to show that in many instances—I avoid saying "all instances," because I know of no absolute proof—you can add to your postulates a new postulate and deduce a new set of theorems richer than before. This being the case, you cannot reason from the fact that the conservation of energy or any such law is applicable with exactness to biological phenomena, to the conclusion that this law is sufficient to predetermine the behavior of organisms. If you have an intuition that you can, this intuition is probably false. Sufficiency has to be proved in each case.

I can take time to deduce only one conclusion from this, namely, that a mechanistic explanation of phenomena is always a matter of claiming *sufficiency* for certain laws and never merely one of claiming their *necessity*. I think if you will examine, you will find the word "determinism" has no meaning whatever until you tell what kind of determinism you are talking about. The only significance I have been able to attach to the unqualified word "determinism" is that the universe at time p is absolutely identical with the universe at time q, and I don't think you need much metaphysics to prove this is unmeaning. Determinism is always used with an implied qualification; for example you mean physical-chemical determinism. This means that the laws of physics and chemistry are sufficient to enable you to deduce what is going to happen. This is what is generally called mechanism. Anyone who said that biological phenomena were subject to physical-chemical laws, but also to other laws as well, would, I suppose, have to be called a vitalist. It is thus, I think, true, though paradoxical, that you can escape from mechanism by multiplying laws instead of by doing away with any of them. You have to establish mechanism and refute such vitalism, by showing not merely that physical-chemical laws are necessary, but that they are sufficient. Strangely enough, this cannot be done by those methods of which physical science is so proud, namely observation and careful measurement. Observation and measurement will show that physical-chemical laws are true within the limits of error; they will never prove they are sufficient. Sufficiency can only be proved by deduction, by a complete deduction of the events before the fact. Mechanism may be true, but the proof of it is less easy than might at first appear.

January 20, 1914

ટ~ NOTES

[*?Royce*]: *Boston Herald* reporter [sic] on Henderson.

[*Royce*, citing an anecdote]: "A hypothesis is a proposition with an 'if' in it, and you make it to have something to reason about. You verify it by drawing a diagram and if you verify it often enough the light of truth and reality dawns upon you."

Mr. Troland: [Note.] [30] In biology our natural thinking is saturated with the intuition of purpose. Cf. Darwin's theory. Fitness and the survival thereof are almost self-evident, but were not brought forward, because of purposive ideas. Darwin's discovery was that no organism is perfect, simply some were better than others. The Darwinian doctrine itself is often stated in half-teleological terms. Organization and fitness retain teleological flavor. Various abstract logical systems; if we could invent such a system corresponding to biology, we should be able to remove traces of teleology. Parallel entities, [and] complexes which differ in degree of complexity and in form. Operation definable called interaction. Outcome determined by degree of complexity and forms, opposed and unopposed. When opposed forms interact, the result is a destruction of complexes and creation of more complexes, each less elaborate, etc. The unopposed would survive—analogy with natural selection and development. Mechanical system will produce appearance of teleology.

Royce: Present movement (neo-vitalistic) is teleological. James's concept of a trap (1884–85, written earlier). A trap permits accretions of a certain sort, like a sieve. The filter thus itself alters. Or-

[30] See footnote 67, p. 184, below.

ganisms may act like traps. ([Written] in safe place, margin of a copy of Spencer.) C. M. Williams, introduction to [her book on] evolution and ethics; Fechner, appearance of the seemingly purposive; Spencer's theory of the "plastic body." Convenient example of trap is a pile of brushwood in a stream bed, much interwoven, grows and propagates, very strong after the freshets.

Discussion of Dr. Costello's note [in his summary of the previous meeting].

Brogan: [Note.] Plato and Aristotle and historical method. Question of control of the personal equation. Philological methods are exact, recognized; little difference of conclusions. When investigators enter philosophic discussion, then difficulty. Shorey's opinion: (1) A scholar must be alive to the philosophic problems. (2) Must have Socratic ignorance. Case of Zeller [in *Die Philosophie der Griechen*]: Zeller on teleology. Aristotle's teleology is "a good is attained"; Zeller's teleology is purposive.

Royce: Brogan is too hasty in criticizing Zeller.

Brogan: We can test (1) interest and (2) freedom from prejudice. There are things in the author [which] one does not see, sources of error.

Eliot: Average perversion. Can you measure these things?

Royce: Zeller lacks dramatic and synthetic character. But was skeptical, without definite opinions. Fischer is dramatic. Schopenhauer said history of philosophy showed what happened when the thought of a philosopher had passed into the narrow brain of a German professor.

Brogan: They have ways of thinking in which they see things. Burnet is philologist as yet. Shorey hedonist, nominalist, utilitarian; therefore Plato also.[31]

Royce: Anthropological and cultural methods. Hence treats philosopher as an instance of *life*. Meyer's *Geschichte des Altertums;* Burnet's *Early Greek Philosophy*. Cf. J. Schmidt, *Geschichte des geistigen Lebens in Deutschland;* Heym, history of romantic school

---

[31] A marginal note seems to indicate that Brogan also cited Constantine Ritter and Otto Apelt.

[*Die romantische Schule*] (history on background of politics, social life, etc.). See thinker on a background.

January 20, 1914

ॐ SUMMARY

The meeting opened with the reading of a charming little clipping from the *Boston Herald*, purporting to be a summary of a paper read by Professor Henderson at the Johns Hopkins.[32] This fragment of misinformation suggested to Professor Royce several similar anecdotes.

Mr. Troland then presented the first sketch of some work on which he was engaged: that of showing by a purely formal logical construction how, from premises of a mechanistic nature, one could deduce consequences which would simulate teleology. Of

---

[32] From the *Boston Herald*, January 20, 1914, p. 1, col. 2: "BELIEVES LIFE IN INORGANIC MATTER. DR. HENDERSON OF HARVARD SPRINGS STARTLING THEORY ON JOHNS HOPKINS SAVANTS. (Special Despatch to *The Herald*.) Baltimore, Jan. 19—Before a distinguished group of scientists in the Johns Hopkins Hospital laboratory, this afternoon, Dr. L. J. Henderson of Harvard asserted that researches extending over many years had convinced him that inorganic matter contained latent life.

"Before the surprised savants who heard this radical theory had recovered from their astonishment he added that he believed this latent life became active under certain conditions, and that soon the life [sic] between the two forms of existence would be crossed.

"Dr. Henderson combatted the old theory that life sprang into existence and adapted itself to its environments, such a theory being one that no one understood or ever could understand. It involved an inexplicable theory that had no scientific basis, and its assumption was only an excuse for not making any progress in the study of evolution. He would assume, therefore, that there were certain conditions which would be favorably adapted to the origin of active matter and his researches had led him to believe there were such conditions."

this logical construction he had at present only the ground plan.
He presented the situation as follows. In biology our natural thinking is saturated with the intuition of purpose. Such terms as *organization* and *fitness* retain a teleological flavor, and Darwin's anti-
teleological theories are often stated in half-teleological terms.
What Darwin really said was that certain organisms were different
from others, with the result that some survived and others did not
—in this there is no teleology. If we could devise an abstract logical
system corresponding to biology, we should be able to eliminate this
intuition of purpose, just as the geometers have been able to eliminate certain misleading intuitions of space. Such a system would
consist of simple entities and of complexes, the latter differing in
degree of complexity and in form. We might then define an operation called "interaction," and deduce the outcome of applying the
operation to the various types of complexes. The interaction operations would be some of a sort we may call "opposed" and some "unopposed." When "opposed" interactions occur, the result is a destruction of complexes and the creation of more numerous, less
elaborate, complexes. The unopposed complexes would, on inter-
acting, survive.

Professor Royce, in comment, remarked that the present tendency seemed to be teleological, neo-vitalistic. As a case of mechanism simulating purpose, he then mentioned Professor James'
conception of a "trap." What a trap is, is illustrated by the pile of
driftwood in a mountain torrent, which acts like a sieve, catching
certain sorts of material, letting other sorts go by, so that it thus
grows in a way which might almost seem the result of purpose.
Organisms may be cases of traps.

After a further discussion of mechanism, suggested by the report
on the previous meeting, Mr. Brogan read a paper on the interpretation of Plato and Aristotle by the historians of philosophy. The
philological methods are exact and recognized and lead to comparatively little difference of conclusions. But when philosophical questions are raised, the historian has to be a philosopher if he is fairly
to understand them, but being a philosopher he is likely to mis-

represent a philosophy other than his own. If he does not actually distort it, he will nevertheless give a wrong impression by ignoring what from his philosophical viewpoint does not appear important. Conclusion: (1) a scholar and historian must be alive to all philosophic problems, but (2) about any of them he must possess Socratic ignorance.

The discussion turned especially on the case of Zeller. Professor Royce maintained that Mr. Brogan was too harsh in his criticisms; Zeller was lacking in dramatic and synthetic instincts, but as regards philosophical opinions he was simply a somewhat skeptical inquirer. Mr. Brogan maintained that Zeller, nevertheless, had ways of thinking, if not positive opinions, of his own (as shown, for example, in his misinterpretation of Aristotle's view of teleology) and he showed inability to appreciate certain aspects of thought (as in his ignoring of Plato's aesthetics). At the close of the discussion Professor Royce called attention to the method of writing the history of philosophy which tries to eliminate the personal equation by considering the subject always on a background of the culture and general political and social history of the times.

The next meeting was to be a general symposium on the question of the contrast, if any, between description and explanation.

February 10, 1914

ह≫ NOTES

Description and explanation.

Dr. Van Riper: [Note.] What is necessary for our understanding of the facts is necessary for the facts themselves. Hence all truth is interrelated. Hence there are not two different kinds of truth, description and explanation. But there might be a relative distinction into overlapping classes. Only at a late stage in thought does explanation get separated from description. Does not discovery of law raise new problems? Is it then an explanation? To say some things have others like them is not explanation. Sometimes philosophy is said to be explanatory and general, science descriptive and detailed; but this is an unsatisfactory conclusion. Another faulty account is that which distinguishes acquaintance (description of immediacy) and knowledge about (explanation). Not profitable in this case. Another account says explanation is reduction to more general laws. This is because one feels deduction is more valid. But general laws are descriptive and more uncertain. If a new fact is discovered, it seems that deductive connection with old facts helps certainty. Yes, but it is not a new sort of truth. Satisfaction obtained from general laws; but there may be few all-explaining laws. Explanation is well though not fertilely explained to mean: it is inconceivable that facts be otherwise; it is due to purpose.

Royce: Schiller is wrong (fifty axioms, 1,225 deductions). An infinite of deductions is possible from a finite number of premises. And some can be found only empirically, e.g., primes. Questions of description and explanation arise here. (Why is casting out nines good?) Explanation means reduction to small number of principles. Self-evidence is hereby often destroyed. Self-evidence means "don't know the subject." Self-evidence is atavism, or authority. Russell weak on "evidence." Similarity is an illusion. Enough miracles make a law and the law is clear.

Dr. Woods: But this latter sort helps us to predict. History has only gone to the descriptive stage and not even reached classification. Should we measure fame or influence? First aim is classification in time-and-space correlations—descriptions not at random.

Brogan: [Note.] Question can't be answered directly. We explain logically by analytic definition. We seek by induction the general propositional functions. No real differentiation of explanations and descriptions. If there are any propositions not descriptive, they are elementary propositions. All sciences presuppose logical theory. Methodology is a collection of arts. In most sciences, if not all, an explanation is not different from a description. In psychology there is no real difference between descriptive and other psychology. Wrong to hold that description is recording of the immediate. Always mediary. Teleological explanation? Assertions about value are as descriptive as anything else. The questions of simples and complexes and implication, etc., are important.

Addendum: "Merely an explanation" where general law is not evident but from it a self-evident truth can be deduced.

Royce: Is Woods' notion of causes useful?

Brogan: What is implication? is the question.

Miss Webster: [Note.] "Why?" demands explanation; ambiguous. Description means "How?" Pearson excludes the "Why," [but] there is a use for explanation in natural science. What we can find out by analysis of the given is description; explanation calls further for relations to something beyond, etc. Great number of cases of explanation; all agree in going beyond the given. Explanation is synthesis. [Description and explanation are] distinct but not contradictory.

[*?Royce*]: Other meanings. What is "cause"? What is "reason"?

[*Miss Webster*]: Might be temporal or other systems not necessarily "deductive."

Brogan: [Every] complete system is deductive. (Questioned by Van Riper and Miss Webster.)

Royce: Professor Davis' investigations of Connecticut Valley (*Popular Science Monthly,* 1909 or 1910).[33] Describes [features] and then gives an account of their origin. Hypothesis: grant these [geological] faults in this order. Was this an explanation? Verification followed. Introduces hypothetically something you can't verify directly or now (deduction only incidental). Not observation, descriptive in form nevertheless.

Troland: Typical use of explanation: relation of a successful hypothesis and the facts for which it holds.

---

[33]   W. M. Davis had on occasion been a guest of the seminar. Practically all of his papers on Connecticut geology came out before 1900, and the only one of these published in the *Popular Science Monthly* appeared in 1891 (XL, 221–35) and concerned extinct volcanoes.

Royce: Probability here rises into prominence.

Woods: All my work probability. But another element [is present] in explanation and causation: an explanation is interesting. The interesting and striking reason is what is called for—not the constant, e.g., law of gravitation.

Eliot: No distinction here of description and explanation.

February 10, 1914

ઠ৯ SUMMARY

Topic of the meeting was description and explanation.

Dr. Van Riper read the first paper on this subject. He said that all truth was one interrelated system and thence it could be deduced that description and explanation could not be totally different in nature. One might, of course, make a relative distinction. But such a distinction has arisen historically very late, and in general there is no sound and important difference.

For example it is sometimes said that generalization into law is explanation. If it happens only once, it is a miracle, but if it happen many times, its occurrence is explained. The mere observation of such repetition is obviously not explanation at all; it is merely a number of descriptions grouped together. Secondly, the distinction between acquaintance and knowledge about cannot profitably be identified with the distinction between description and explanation. So also, thirdly, we may object to the identification of explanation with deduction, for deduction is from the general, and empirical general laws are descriptions, and uncertain into the bargain. Other cases also, such as proving the contradictory self-contradictory, or treating facts teleologically, are in science not at present sufficiently widely applied, to cause us to identify explanation with these. The conclusion is that there is no important distinction between description and explanation.

A discussion followed, in which Professor Royce took objection to a quotation from F. C. S. Schiller mentioned by Dr. Van Riper to the effect that fifty premises gave only 1,225 possible deductions. Professor Royce then added that the contrast of description and explanation was not the exclusive property of the natural sciences, but seemed to appear even in pure mathematics. Prime numbers we can study only by a sort of empirical description without explanation—explanation being here identified with deduction from a few general principles. These principles need not be self-evident, self-evidence being rather an indication that one does not know the subject. Dr. Woods objected to Dr. Van Riper's opinion that general laws do not explain, but simply say there are many cases like a given case. Dr. Woods held that a general law aided us to predict, and thus had a practical importance which was not possessed by the single case. History does not enable us to predict because it is not in the explanatory stage—indeed it is not even in the descriptive stage of mere classification.

Mr. Brogan read the second paper. He said the question of explanation was dependent upon more ultimate questions. These questions were questions of logic, such as the nature of simples and complexes, of implication, etc. Until we had a more philosophical account than we now possess of how members of a system are bound together by implication, we shall not know what an explanation should seek after. Also, there is no such thing as mere direct description, but all description is mediate, and involves going beyond the given. Ordinary usage is very vague, and instead of making explanation more adequate, it says "This is a possible explanation" when it refers to a guess at the cause of an event; whereas were one perfectly sure he would say he was simply describing. As regards identifying explanation with a teleological account, Mr. Brogan did not see why precise assertions about values were not, when obtainable, as purely descriptive as were assertions about facts.

Miss Webster read the third paper. Explanation, it is currently said, answers "Why" and description "How," but these terms are ambiguous. She preferred to denominate description what could be found out by analysis of given data, and to use explanation when there was reference to something beyond the given. Description is analysis, explanation is synthesis.

A discussion then followed. Miss Webster maintained that there were synthetic systems which were not deductive, so that she did not mean by explanation deduction. Mr. Brogan held that every complete system was deductive.

Professor Royce then gave an example from Professor Davis' work in geology, an example of hypothesis, deduction, and verification, and threw out the query whether that was a case of explanation. It went beyond the observable both in time and space, particularly in time, since it referred to a time prior to the coming of man on the globe, and yet as regards the subject-matter it was capable of description had anyone been there to describe. Mr. Troland said the typical scientific use of explanation is the relation of a successful hypothesis to the facts for which it holds.

Dr. Woods, after some remarks about estimation of probability with reference to hypotheses, entered upon a new discussion. In all cases of explanation and search after causes, he said, what we are really seeking are the interesting and striking factors. Thus when a book falls, it is not interesting to refer it to something so commonplace as the law of gravitation; we are more concerned to learn that two philosophers were quarrelling and the book got knocked down in the fracas which followed. (The examples which he gave were all of such particular events of a historical character, i.e., belonging to the concrete rather than to the abstract sciences. Of course if you are seeking the explanation for a unique individual occurrence, you are very apt to look for some antecedent uniqueness in the circumstances. The historian ceases to be a historian as soon as his ultimate aim ceases to be the individual occurrences which never recur. The physicist or sociologist is seeking, on the contrary, for universal laws as such, and the abstract description of large groups and masses of similar phenomena.)

February 17, 1914

ॐ NOTES

Royce: Last meeting—*explanation* was some kind of synthesis, teamwork of various *descriptions*. Connection between two apparently distinct lines of description might be called explanation; there are different kinds of description, and explanation unites.

In physics one uses "models." They are hypotheses of the second grade. One has already hypothetical descriptions, e.g., mathematical laws, kinetic theory of gases, ether. Have we a right to such models? asked Ostwald. Lord Kelvin said he never was really interested in a physical hypothesis unless he could conceive a model of it. Models in heredity (Mendelian). Model not equivalent to hypothesis. A model is a figure of a familiar sort. If one uses differential equations, in so far there is no model (electro-magnetic theory). Enriques says physics has used (1) optical models and (2) tactile-muscular models. Force is a case of (2). Molecular-atomic accounts are (1). Mach, Kirchhoff, Ostwald prefer not to use models and to speak of descriptions. Energists use no models, use "prototheses"—predictions, not models; but can be verified as models cannot. The abstractions are very abstract and indirect, but can be verified. We may use the term *explanation* for models.

Van Riper: Stochastic vs. formal hypotheses—Alexander Smith.

Royce: "Leading idea" is an unverifiable, irrefutable hypothesis —indestructible hypothesis. Such is valuable if it turns attention to objects one would not otherwise study.

Costello: English physicists use models.

Troland: Every physical hypothesis is an existence postulate. All are stochastic. Perrin on Brownian movement. Radioactivity.

Royce on Ostwald.

Troland: [Note.] Description is a somewhat arbitrary symbolic representation in language. [Its] function [is] representative; should be analytic. Explanation is synthetic; used in connection with hypotheses. We introduce objects we believe to exist but do not observe. We thus proceed as by a sort of coherent imagination and thus are able to bring together the pieces of a chopped-up puzzle. A hypothesis is not a formal symbolic affair. Cases of explanation are: sub-conscious mechanisms, e.g., Freudian; atomic; electronic. Temporal pictures, etc., are hypotheses. Description: relation between symbol and object—analytic. Explanation: an imaginal model.

Royce: What gives the pattern its character of wholeness? Peirce said signs were indices, icons (explanations?), symbols (descriptions). Guidance is of three kinds: Point to a thing—street name at the corner, shop sign on the shop—these are *indices;* constant but elementary use in science. *Icon* is a pattern, an image, a picture, a diagram, a map. *Symbols* need a habit for connection with objects, often a convention. Symbol as symbol is a substitute for, not an attachment to an object; e.g., an algebra.

Herbart's psychology was symbolic. *Vorstellungen* were symbols. Freud, etc., are Herbartian but more empirical.

Costello: Abstract is descriptive and concrete is explanatory.

Royce: Analytic and synthetic in mathematics. Cases of these. Process of finding one's course at sea is a synthetic process.

Two weeks: Miss Webster. Explanation, etc., continued next week.

February 17, 1914

ஜ SUMMARY

A continuation of the discussion on explanation and description. Professor Royce, in summarizing the previous meeting, said the general conclusion seemed to be that explanation was some kind of synthesis—for example, "teamwork" of various descriptions. Any connection between two apparently distinct lines of description might be called an explanation.

Next, Professor Royce referred to another point, the use of models in physical explanations. If one has reached hypothetical descriptions, for instance mathematical laws applying to phenomena, and if one then endeavors to see more clearly the reason for this particular combination of laws, he may do so by constructing a model, which may take the form of a machine or collection of mechanical parts. Lord Kelvin's opinion was quoted that he never was really interested in a physical hypothesis unless he could get a model of it, and this is true of other English physicists. On the Continent analytic methods prevail more largely, and descriptions, e.g., in terms of differential equations, are preferred to so-called explanations. Energists such as Ostwald object to "hypotheses," meaning thereby the explanations in terms of models, which latter they say can never be verified, and prefer to them "prototheses"—that is, predictions in themselves abstract, for instance regarding energy conditions, but such as can be verified to any degree of precision by exact measurements. Energy is a very abstract concept, but the laws of energy can be verified to an extent to which the apparently more concrete and empirical molecular theory cannot. Further characteristics of models and their use are suggested by Enriques' distinction between optical models, such as atomic theories, and tactile-muscular models, such as forces. Models may be used in other sciences than physics, for example in Mendelian theories of heredity.

Dr. Van Riper inquired the relation of this to a distinction made by Alexander Smith of Chicago between stochastic or verifiable hypotheses, that is, hypotheses concerning the existence of observable phenomena, and formal hypotheses. (As I understand, the laws of motion would be cases of formal hypotheses, there being no concrete case, for instance, of a body moving in a perfectly straight line.) Mr. Brogan asked if "formal hypothesis" was identical with what Professor Royce has called "leading idea" or "unverifiable hypothesis." Professor Royce replied in the negative, since a leading idea was not only unverifiable but irrefutable, and it is valuable chiefly for the way in which it directs attention to objects which might be overlooked. Smith's "formal hypotheses" seemed to be hypotheses which could be refuted, but which can never be verified except by indirect means, and thus might all the while be merely convenient fictions to which nothing in the physical world corresponded.

Mr. Troland maintained that every physical hypothesis contains an existence postulate; all are stochastic in the sense that they all, whether stated in universal or particular propositions, indicate something which could be experienced, even though not actually experienced. Mr. Troland then read the paper he had written on "Description and Explanation." A description is a somewhat arbitrary symbolic representation in language. It is a product of analysis of the observed data and its function is representative. Explanation is not symbolic but is a synthetic hypothesis which introduces objects we believe to exist but do not observe. We imagine what must be the nature of the coherent whole which shall bring together the fragments we observe. It is as if we were called upon to put together a chopped-up puzzle of which many of the pieces are not obtainable by us. A hypothesis, in this sense, is not a formal symbolic affair, but is a postulate of the existence of a reality of which we can form a model in the imagination through a sort of synthetic intuition.

Questions by Dr. Costello brought out that Mr. Troland thought an explanatory hypothesis was not a methodological device, such as a model often is, but was a belief regarding the nature and pattern of reality. The difference between description and explanation is the difference between the abstract and the concrete.

Professor Royce called attention to Charles Peirce's theory of signs. According to Peirce, signs are either indices (e.g., a street name at the corner, a shop sign on the shop), or icons (e.g., patterns, models, images, pictures, diagrams; hence explanations, in

Mr. Troland's sense, have an analogy with icons), or thirdly, symbols (corresponding to Mr. Troland's descriptions). A symbol is somewhat arbitrarily attached to an object either through habit or convention, but its office is rather to lead one away from the object. It may be used as a substitute for the object, for instance in an algebra. Professor Royce, in closing, called attention to the contrast between analytic or symbolic methods in mathematics and synthetic or intuitional methods.

Comment: Mr. Troland identifies a description with a symbolic expression; Professor Royce identifies a symbol with a substitute for an object, which substitute may then be treated separately, as in an algebra. The conclusion that a description takes one away from the object described, seems nevertheless contrary to usage. Further distinctions seem necessary. Peirce, in his own treatment in Baldwin's *Dictionary*, says an icon (e.g., a picture) would retain its character, the character which makes it a sign, though it had neither object nor interpreter; a symbol requires both. To put it in brief, a symbol essentially has to do with knowledge, not so an icon. I doubt if this is a workable distinction. I should be disposed to say an icon, like an index, has relation to the sensory side of consciousness, a symbol to the motor side; an icon you perceive, a symbol you do something with. I should then say symbols are of two types: indicative symbols and substitutive symbols. An indicative symbol resembles an index, though it is not physically attached to the object, but only by way of knowledge. It is an instrument by means of which you can get in touch with the actual objects, a "leading" in the pragmatic sense. Such symbols enable you to handle objects better, just as you can handle live coals better if you have a pair of tongs. It is bound up with a habit of acting, being perhaps itself a fragment of an inhibited act. It can be used to convey information to others in a way analogous to that by which an actualized action is conveyed to others by imitation. A description uses this kind of symbols, and thus does *not* move away from the object described. Substitutive symbols take one away from the objects. A mathematical, so-called analytic, calculus is of this sort. The form and structure of a group of such symbols should parallel accurately the systematic form and structure of the objects represented, else their value as substitutes is destroyed. But this similarity of pattern between symbols and objects gives them an analogy to icons. You can thus follow the symbolic structure for its own sake, as in the somewhat automatic performance of ordinary arithmetical operations, and then at the end, owing to the parallelism, you can read the result in terms of cubic yards, or dollars and cents.

Having made the above distinctions, I find myself unable fully to subscribe to Mr. Troland's opinion that description is symbolic and explanation an intuition of reality. I should say that in both cases symbols and reality are both present, and substitutive symbols, in so far as they take us away from the objects, are neither description nor explanation. I should agree that description is analytic, but for me analysis and abstraction are distinguishable; I should agree that explanation is more synthetic, and I agree there is at least a close psychological relation between synthesis and intuition, though again I should not identify the two. I may add that both analysis and synthesis, as movements from whole to part and part to whole, have to do with knowledge, with the relation of our symbols to the objects as known by us—they have to do with knowledge, and are in themselves neither a making nor an unmaking of the complexes which are known.

I have come to look upon both description and explanation as parts of the larger inductive process of science, which is, as a whole, *an analysis which distinguishes in the real world terms and relations.* I should define induction in terms of this analysis and not in terms of the probability of its results. How far the relational analysis is adequate to reality is for metaphysics to say; I shall simply take it somewhat realistically as the obtaining knowledge of, and symbolic formulations for, a structure which reality actually possesses. But I seem to observe, somewhat inductively and as a hypothesis verified by diverse experiences, a difference among relations; that is, if I may borrow the terminology of certain current discussions, some relations seem to make more difference to their terms than do others—they are more internal. For this reason I disagree with what I believe is the almost universally accepted opinion among philosophers that for the scientist, once he has abstracted from values, one fact is as good as another. It seems to me, on the contrary, that—defining a fact as a complex of terms united by a relation—there is a *factual hierarchy among facts*. This difference among facts is due solely to the degree of internality of the relation concerned; it is an ontological and not a valuational difference, and has, so far as I can see, absolutely nothing to do with values, or with our desires, purposes, and preferences. I repeat, I am not talking about anything I should call values or purposes. The only purpose relevant to it is the purpose of the pure scientist, the purpose to understand the phenomena as they are. This difference among relations from what seems like complete externality to any amount of internality, is not something which necessarily appears on first observation. But the evidence for it seems to me as great as the evidence for, let us say, the existence of an atomic structure of matter, which, also, is scarcely something that stands revealed to immediate inspection. Now description is that process which primarily treats facts as all on a level. When its analysis comes upon certain relations as more central and essential, relations which are the key to a given group of phenomena, explanation takes up the more synthetic study of the way in which these key-relations determine the various observed and observable aspects of the concrete phenomena.

With me all roads recently have led to Rome, and I have encountered the demand for some such distinction among relations and facts, as to their objective ontological importance, in at least the following directions: (1) the question of the nature of organization; (2) the question of the relation of facts to values; (3) the question of the relation of knowledge to reality and of the proper use of symbols; (4) the question of the relation of mathematics to empirical facts; (5) the question of the nature of analysis; (6) the question of the task of induction; (7) the question as to what it is, which has so persistently sent men hunting after what are generally called the causes of events and which is not solved completely by replacing causes with laws, for there arises (8) the question of the true nature of scientific law; (9) the question of the nature of implication and whether any true proposition implies another true proposition, and how you would best contradict an implication; (10) the question of the nature of logical demonstration; (11) the question what was really aimed at by Aristotle in seeking to have universal propositions the expression of *necessary* connections; (12) the question what is the nature of that fertility or fruitfulness which certain mathematical formulae undoubtedly possess as over against others, and (13) the nature of that characteristic of mathematical definitions which Whitehead and Russell indicate on pp. 11–12 of the Introduction to the *Principia* by the word "important" when they say: "In spite of the fact that definitions are theoretically superfluous, it is nevertheless true that they often convey more important information than is contained in the propositions in which they are used. This arises [because] a definition usually implies that the *definiens* is worthy of careful consideration [and] embodies . . . our judgment as to what is most important"; (14) the question as to what is the ultimate basis of the logical notion of relevance and the closely related concept of "universe of discourse"; and (15) the question as to the proper basis for the classification of the sciences. These are questions, almost all of them, questions of science as well as of metaphysics, and they all hang together on a single thread. A problem of such enormous scope cannot be dealt with in a couple of sentences. I simply indicate that it is against the background of this greater problem I see problem number (16), the question of the proper distinction between description and explanation.

February 24, 1914

৯৯ NOTES

Royce: Relation of symbols to reality. Case of fractions. First,
iconic relation to quantity; later, freed from quantity.

Costello: Relation to symbols not thus settled.

Royce: [Assignment.] New set of short papers. Of what use is
the presupposition that events have causes? Legal search for causes:
Mr. Prescott Hall on notion of "proximate cause" in legal history
—insurance law; insured against damage from a certain cause—
published in *The Green Bag*.[34] Case of disease and health, responsibility, etc. What cause is, is metaphysics. But methodologically,
what is the use or uses for the search after causes? Might be connected with scientific law. "Some uses of the conception of cause
and the search for causes"; "Nature and definition of the search
for causes"—in two weeks from this time. Cf. view of Schopenhauer
[in] "The Fourfold Root": Schopenhauer said search for causes
characteristic of the understanding. Physical causes are of events.
Search for cause is for what by rule is followed by the event. All intelligent creatures, e.g. dogs, look for causes.

Sen Gupta: [Note.] Description and explanation. Answer to
child: They happen because they do happen—explanation by uniformity. In chemical analysis, explanation by analysis. Teleological
is a third type of explanation. Three pure types. A good explanation has all three. No sharp distinction between description and explanation, except [as regards] part and whole: an explanation defines a system.

Eliot: [Note.] Description and explanation. Difference of act

---

[34] An error for the *Harvard Law Review*, XV (March, 1902), 541–67; the
article was entitled "Some Observations on the Doctrine of Proximate Cause."

rather than of content. Explanation: law, cause, [reality behind] illusion, metaphysical interpretation. A description alters. An explanation tries to maintain one point of view; impossible. Description is more sophisticated than explanation: one seeks, among savages, an internal kinship, not one of resemblance; first explanation. Explanation is often by cause and effect, then ground and consequence; identical. Cause becomes [form of relation of] universal [to] particular, then becomes description. Case and law need in turn to be related. In end, no matter of fact. No illusion is ever explained, by any theory of knowledge. If you treat illusion as real, you get nowhere.

Description is just as bad as explanation. Pure contemplation [is] only an ideal case. You give a valuation and interpretation. Description is science, relatively metaphysical explanation. In Absolute both meet. In a scientist the distinction is not important. Points-of-view monadology.[35]

Royce: Bradley held the last view. Description deals with the particular, you say.

Eliot: Explanation deals with a transition, experiences a particular-universal transition.

Royce: Explanation (primitive) by relation to a will.

Eliot: Primitive consciousness luxuriates in the feeling of explanation.

Royce: Another [kind of] explanation is fatalistic: things happen thus because they once began to happen thus. It "took to" happening.

Eliot: Craving for explanation, not a description.

Royce: One finds a content [i.e., satisfaction] in origin stories. Inversion of uniformity. Why this uniformity?

[35] A marginal note, relating apparently to the final part of Eliot's paper, reads: "Not wholly false nor true that an explanation is wholly wrong."

February 24, 1914
៩ SUMMARY

Professor Royce first led a brief discussion on some topics brought up by the report of the previous meeting, particularly as to the sense in which a set of symbols must resemble in structure that system of which they are symbolic.

He then assigned, as the topic for a set of short papers for March 10, the general subject: "Of what methodological uses is the presupposition that events have causes?" He mentioned the legal usages of the term "cause" as explained by Mr. Prescott Hall of Boston in this seminary in a previous year; also Schopenhauer's doctrine as presented in his work "The Fourfold Root of the Principle of Sufficient Reason." The discussion of March 10 is to be methodological rather than metaphysical, and the papers are to be as constructive as possible.

Two short papers on description and explanation were then read. The first, by Mr. Sen Gupta, said that explanation might be of three types: (1) in terms of uniformity (e.g., where one tells a child this event happened as it did because they always do happen thus), (2) by analysis, (3) in teleological terms. The most satisfying explanations contain all three of these factors. An explanation often defines a system within which the event falls, but there is no sharp distinction between description and explanation.

The second paper, by Mr. Eliot, said the difference between description and explanation was in the act rather than in the content. Explanation is more primitive, description more sophisticated. Explanation tries, though always unsuccessfully, to confine itself to one point of view. We may seek to explain in terms of a cause, or a law, or by seeking the reality back of an illusion, or by a metaphysical interpretation. That in terms of which a phenomenon is explained seldom resembles it, but is supposed linked to it by some inner causal kinship—for instance, explanations in terms of will. The primitive mind has a native craving for explanations, luxuriates in the feeling of explanation. Causal explanations tend to go over to the form of relation of universal to particular, and, as the tendency to transcend the given continues to diminish, finally explanation is transformed into description. The failure of all explanation in the case of illusions is particularly striking.

But description is in as bad a case as explanation. The act of describing brings alteration of the object described, and the case of pure contemplation is an ideal limit we never attain. What we get is a monadology of points of view, each point of view carrying with it its own interpretation and valuation of the real world. To sum up, explanation is an act which tries with indifferent success to bring the particular under the universal; description tries to stay in the particular as given, but in spite of itself transforms the given by the interpretation it gives to it.

Professor Royce called attention to a contrast among primitive peoples between the explanations in terms of voluntary will, and a more fatalistic explanation in terms of a first case. In the latter type of explanations, one finds contentment in stories of the first origin of things and events. One says they first happened so-and-so, and after that they just "took to happening" and therefore have happened just so ever since. Uniformity, instead of presenting a complete solution, first presents a problem as to why this particular sort of uniformity; but the problem is solved so soon as one discovers why it happened thus the first time, and the later uniform occurrence is considered as natural and only to be expected.

March 3, 1914

&⤳ NOTES

7:55–8:17—twenty-two minutes.

Mr. Hefelbower: [Note.] [36] History of philosophy. Relation of
John Locke to English deism. Deism 1696–1740, perhaps 1754. A
method is a means to accomplish a purpose. Purposes are relative
to a certain field of interest. A method is determined by the materials and by the problem; materials and purpose. No methods in the
abstract. In this problem, two lines of investigation: (1) comparison, (2) collection and interpretation of historical data, relations of
writers, contents of contemporaries. Toland and Tindal influenced
by Locke's doctrine of ideas. Is rationalism in the orthodox party?
What are you comparing? What is deism? Locke is located, not so
deism. We must study it on the background of the thought, life, of
the time: e.g., toleration. We must consider the poly-dimensional
character of history. Toleration was not confined to Locke and
deists. Hooker, Platonists, rational theologians, latitudinarians.
E.g., reasonableness: Is Locke a deist in this respect? Cambridge
Platonists, Tillotson, Sherlock say same thing; even Hooker. What
is the viewpoint?—(1) political and economical, (2) theologico-
religious (four to five thousand pamphlets, 1660–1685), (3) scientific (Boyle, Newton, Sydenham), (4) philosophical (few: Locke,
Platonists, Hobbes). Across these four fields two tendencies: (1)
conservative, traditional, vs. (2) radical, critical, rationalistic, liberal. Any man or movement can be defined in these terms. Locke
is [in] politics liberal, [in] theology conservative except in method,

[36] Based on Hefelbower's dissertation, afterwards published, *The Relation of
John Locke to English Deism* (Chicago, 1918). Hefelbower had presented a
paper on historical method in the seminar of 1911–12.

[in] other two [fields] rationalistic. Fight against Oxford scholasticism (to 1692). Deists no interest in (1) politics; in method radical as Locke in (2) religion and also in results; nothing in (3)
science; Toland did a little in (4) philosophy, but very little. No
question therefore about (1) or (3) or about conservatives.

Difficulty: deistic, those practically universally regarded as
such; then determine later, e.g., is Shaftesbury a deist? Tillotson
(often quoted)? Locke? Chillingworth (in 1640's)? But this comparison we wish to make is needed for the definition, and the definition for comparison. What method? What conclusion did they
reach?

Royce: What of Leslie Stephen?

Hefelbower: (Details [concerning Stephen's *English Thought in
the Eighteenth Century*].)

Royce: Good introduction to seventeenth-century thought: Mark
Pattison in *Essays and Reviews*—"Tendencies of Religious Thought
in England, 1688–1750." McGiffert, *Protestant Thought Before
Kant,* is good but solely theological. Scholasticism—what type
was it?

Hefelbower [cites] Bourne, [*Life of John Locke*]; Höffding, [sc.
History of Modern Philosophy]; and Windelband, [*A History of
Philosophy*]. Disgust with Middle Ages. But, 1570 on, scholasticism
revived in universities. Monkish Aristotle at Oxford.

Royce: What textbooks?

Hefelbower: Under ban, Descartes.

Royce: Great textbook of scholasticism was *Disputations* of
Suárez; tries to unify Scotists and Thomists. Jesuit; not used at
Oxford. What text did Locke use? Background you emphasize; (1)
ethical movement you omit (Hobbes to Adam Smith and Hume)
[and] (2) history of nonconformity. [Cites] Baumann, *Die Lehren
von Raum, Zeit und Mathematik in der neueren Philosophie.* Importance of Suárez; Descartes trained upon it.[37]

Hefelbower: Under religion, natural vs. revealed; then view that

---

[37] See Costello's anecdote in *A Philosophy of the Real and the Possible*, p. 90,
about Suárez, Royce, and President Eliot.

ethics is center of religion. Cambridge Platonists opposed Hobbes' ethics. Ethics slowly separated from religion.

Royce: Scholasticism much interested in natural religion, so deists were not new in this. Hermann Reuter, *Geschichte der religiösen Aufklärung im Mittelalter.* "Deism" of Middle Ages.

Royce: Was engaged in preparing a paper for Dr. Southard, Dr. Henderson, naturalists, and medical men. Two or three times a year on vitalism, etc. Technical. Paper emphasizes causation. Will be read here first.[38]

"The Mechanical, the Historical and the Statistical":—Vitalism often [means the hypothesis that] phenomena of living organisms [are] like conscious deliberation and choice—different from machines. Materialism opposed. Greatest Greek vitalist Aristotle. Present interest in vitalism. Neglected aspect of Greek vitalism: seems *as if* guided by design. Many vitalists thought nature blindly purposive, though even divine in its skill. Aristotle noted nature was not creative piecemeal by trial and error. Aristotle's God was not a creator. A natural process of imitating a divine perfection. No designs of God or man, but like instinct or genius. Blind mechanism vs. conscious deliberation has seldom been the clear contrast. The *élan vital* was known to the Greeks.

Three types of methods of knowledge. Clerk Maxwell in a paper used this classification. Three kinds of objects of natural science: historical, mechanisms, [and] statistically defined assemblages; and three corresponding methods. Concluding passage [of his treatise] *Theory of Heat,* and [his] article on "Molecules" [39] in *Encyclopaedia Britannica* [ninth edition]; [cf.] Merz, [*A History of European Thought in the Nineteenth Century*], [Vol.] II, eleventh

---

[38] On the following day, March 4, Royce wrote to Peirce and sent him a copy of this paper. In his letter he spoke of having already read the paper before a group of seventeen colleagues who were members of a society formed for scientific discussion; see the extract in Cotton, *Royce on the Human Self,* p. 302. Probably that second reading had been given on the evening of March 4. The paper was published in *Science,* N.S. XXXIX (April 17, 1914), 551–66.

[39] An error for "Atom."

chapter.[40] Confine ourselves to events: historical when individual events or complexes of them; mechanical when invariant laws are studied; statistical when [science] studies averages and always variable probabilities. (1) Event; (2) law, not event as such; (3) neither, but an average. Mechanical and vitalistic and a third. Vitalism always historical, unique, novel. Mechanical makes single events points on a curve. Third view contains unique and individual events; a discrete multitude shows law. Not differential equation; a statistical law involves averages: "p of the a's are b"; "probability q that p differs from q [sic] by not more than X." [41] Statistical view of nature is the "insurance" view; cf. treatment of homicide by the three.

Our actual knowledge of vital phenomena is really statistical. Heredity, variation, growth, disease, death, distribution, etc. The logic of insurance and of vitalism the same. In history we have statistical methods; Dr. Woods [demonstrates] a refinement of an old tendency. [That] a has a tendency to lead to b is always a statement of probability. Statistics is so familiar as to blind; and [it has a] logic of its own. Average, approximation, probability go down to roots. Hard to exaggerate importance of these. Wider and deeper than statistical tables, etc. What [Maxwell] had in mind: electricity and magnetism [having been expressed in terms of] defined differential equations, compute consequences [and] compare with experiment; mechanical. General theory of energy thus developing; also cases of diffusion of gases and unavailability of energy. Clausius. Maxwell's kinetic theory of gases: not altogether mechanical; at least, logic of probability does not need mechanics. The movement of one molecule is indifferent. The logic of probabilities is controverted. But average behavior of objects is a law (of chance!). In *Theory of Heat:* distribution of molecules is like the distribution of errors of observations. Law of random distribution,

[40] An error for "twelfth chapter." Royce cited pp. 599, 601, and 603; *Science,* N.S. XXXIX, 556.
[41] The published text has: "There is a probability q that c differs from d by not more than such and such an amount—say X"; *ibid.*, p. 557.

"iron necessity of chance." New was the fact that when Maxwell deduced properties he was able to deduce not merely mechanical laws but laws of degradation—second law [of the theory of energy]. Second law is essentially statistical. Physical world tends to pass from less probable to more probable. Energy runs downhill for statistical reasons. Boltzmann points out how theory of probability requires at times some reversals. Arrhenius says nebulae do represent reversals. A law can always be found if complex enough system for probability.

When we deal with mechanisms you say ignorance forces us to be statistical: a substitute. Nautical almanac ideal; mortality table a makeshift: mechanical theories are the canonical forms, laws independent of time. But statistics need not be a substitute. All the organic and social sciences, and most of physics [illustrate knowledge expressed by statistics]. And if we knew [the] world millions of times better, the mortality tables would be better. We never know a mechanical theory exactly. Statistical theories *are* the canonical forms: they are literally the approximately true.

Charles Peirce wrote "The Architecture of Theories," "The Doctrine of Necessity Examined," [and] "The Law of Mind," in *Monist* [1891–1892]. Extension of statistics: aggregation and assimilation statistical. Cf. an aggregate: each [member] with a range of variations; a definable and genuine whole, some more or less systematic tendency towards a mutual "assimilation." Birds of a feather tend to have similar fortunes. Classes tend towards the production of further similarities; law that aggregation tends to further mutual assimilation. If stars are in two drifts moving through each other, then the physical arrangement of tables and photo-catalogues tends to a new assimilation, etc. A theory of the origin of chemical elements will show, as radiant energy shows, assimilation. The fecundity of aggregation: result, a sort of unconscious teleology; changeable aggregates increase in likeness. In the purely logical world we have the theory of probability itself, in physics a statistical law that aggregates evolve in a certain way. (1) Tendency to form aggregates and assimilate, (2) some sort of sorting or selection, e.g., a "trap," (3) tendency to form habits. Suppose these and then a process of evolution: not mechanical. From mere chance [evolution] leads towards the simulation of mechanism, teleological appearance in a certain way. "Fecundity of whatever unites"; tendency towards orderliness. Averages not dry.

[*Royce*]: Kapteyn's "two star-drifts" were founded on statistical collections. Henderson's results are result of an assembling. Radioactivity statistical. Divine activities of *élan vital* are intellectualistic and statistical. Number fundamental; statistics founded on number.

March 3, 1914

ϑ SUMMARY

Mr. Hefelbower began the meeting by reading an eighteen-minute paper on the method of investigating the relation of John Locke to English deism. The reading occupied twenty-two minutes. He said a method must always be determined by the particular nature of the problem in hand and by the particular character of the materials obtainable. In the present problem we need to collect historical data which shall be serviceable for the comparison we wish to make. To that end we must know: first, what are the terms between which we are going to institute a comparison, and second, what comparisons will be significant and important. The difficulty in the former case is, of course, not that of locating Locke, but of knowing just what persons may profitably be classed as deists. To solve this problem we shall first note those who undoubtedly are deists, that is, those to whom everybody would unhesitatingly give this title. We shall then compare the doubtful cases with these clear cases. But then we shall have on our hands two comparisons, the main one of Locke with the deists; the subordinate one, of the doubtful deists with those who are indisputedly classed as deists.

What, now, shall be the nature of such comparison? It is here, in making the comparisons in question, that many historians have fallen into error. They have said Locke was rationalistic and tolerant and so were the deists, and therefore Locke should be classed among the deists. Had they considered the fact that other men and movements of that age were also characterized by rationalism and tolerance; in short, had they not neglected to observe the other now less striking movements and characteristics of the period, they would have seen at once that Locke was not made a deist by resembling the deists on this point. At that time the opposed tendencies of radicalism and conservatism appeared in politics, religion, science, and philosophy, and were not an opposition peculiar to the deistic controversy. It follows that we cannot institute a comparison between Locke and the deists taken in isolation and without comparing both with other movements of the same age. It is, however, possible to limit the scope of the comparison in other ways, for example to the field of religion, and here we find the deists radicals, Locke a radical only in methods, conservative in results. The methodological conclusion seems to be that no comparison is possible in abstraction from the total context, unless we first establish good reasons for making just that abstraction.

Professor Royce inquired about certain topics not specifically mentioned in Mr. Hefelbower's account: the type of scholastic philosophy taught in the age of Locke, the history of nonconformity, and the growth of the English ethical movement, Hobbes to Adam Smith and Hume.

The rest of the meeting was devoted by Professor Royce to reading a paper he had prepared for presentation before a group of naturalists and medical men, and entitled: "The Mechanical, the Historical and the Statistical." The substance of the paper is as follows:

The opposition between naturalism and vitalism has seldom been simple contrast between blind mechanism and conscious deliberation, but ever since the time of Aristotle there has been a tendency towards a middle ground, as though nature were blindly purposive, and ends were actually attained in nature though not foreseen.

Clerk Maxwell classified the methods or standpoints of science into three groups: the mechanical, the historical, and the statistical. When we seek invariant and exact laws, we take the mechanical point of view. When we consider individual events as individual, our point of view is historical. When we consider large averages and estimate probabilities, our attitude is statistical. Mechanism tends to the mechanical point of view, vitalism to the historical; the statistical point of view has the advantage over both that it is able to combine laws with individualities.

Our actual knowledge is really statistical; no law of mechanism is capable of more than statistically probable verification. Therefore it is the statistical rather than the mechanical formula which is the more empirical, and which deserves to be called the *canonical* form of scientific law. We may state it as a general law of nature that the physical world tends to pass from the less probable to the more probable distribution. The second law of thermodynamics, for instance, is essentially statistical, for it is the formulation of such a tendency to pass from the less to the more probable distribution. Whenever we use the word *tendency* we are referring to some statistical or semistatistical probability.

It is argued, as against this, that statistics are a makeshift, due to our ignorance of the exact laws. But the counter-argument is equally plausible; just as owing to our lack of visual acuteness, the surface of still water seems perfectly smooth, perhaps just so it is due to our ignorance that the physical laws seem perfectly exact. Statistical laws have, empirically, at least the great advantage of being verifiable; exact laws, by reason of their very exactness, escape empirical verification.

Charles Peirce has outlined a philosophy of nature presupposing this statistical point of view and capable of statistical verification, wherein natural processes would appear as if guided by purpose. It calls for: (1) a tendency to form aggregates and of the members of such aggregates to "assimilate," that is, to become more alike; (2) some process of sorting or selection, for instance a "trap"; (3) a tendency to form habits. Supposing these, an evolutionary process would result wherein it would appear, at least to the superficial view, *as if* there were purpose and also *as if* there were mechanism.

In closing, Professor Royce cited various examples of the profitable use of statistics in natural science—for example, Kapteyn's stardrifts, and radioactivity.

In comment, I should like to ask in what sense assimilation, selection, and habit are statistical merely? Is this view essentially atomistic, and does it hold that from the philosophy-of-nature viewpoint, apart from a further metaphysics, we must consider everything due to chance? I may add, as a further comment, that this theory seems more physical in its temper, whereas mechanism is more mathematical in temper; statistical laws lack that aesthetic charm which the exact and unalterable laws of a rigid mechanistic determinism undoubtedly possess, the which made the chief appeal of determinism to a Spinoza or a Huxley, and appeals today, for example, to such temperamental thinkers as Professor Santayana.

March 10, 1914

ॐ NOTES

[*Royce*]: Heinrich Weber's theory of causality, in Volume III, *Enzyklopädie der Elementarmathematik* von Weber und Wellstein, [section on] "Prinzipien der Wahrscheinlichkeit."

Statistical defined in terms of finite collections, discrete individuals. Peirce's continuity is non-statistical; not clear—cf. Lowell Lectures. Objective chance at first a reality; present state halfway between this and law. Three tendencies, assimilation; expressible statistically.

Causality:

Miss Webster: [Note.] Especially [in] biology, [cause is a] leading idea in science. Not an accidental relation. Definition of cause at an antecedent stage is too broad and too narrow: [there is also] contemporary cause; e.g., heat causes expansion. Causation by future impossible by this [the antecedent] view—Palmer. Necessity denied—Pearson. [Should be] reduced to functions—Mach. Equations. Nevertheless cause [is] a good experimental guide. Cause as probability will grow in importance: "probability [that] A will be followed by B is great" is [a] cause. All events have, in a broad sense, a vast number of causes—too broad. What is really sought? Last change before? Last event before a war is often unimportant, lacking qualification. *The* cause—is there any such thing? Driesch: stimuli too narrow. Jennings: one single cause can be found for the difference between two similar events, but not for the events (method of difference of Mill)—a preceding difference to which present difference is due and [which] can be found experimentally. Experiment is the process of finding this. Cause and probability grouped together by Poincaré [and] by Pearson. Induction gives us probability.

Brogan: "Indispensable" in Mill's sense?

[*Miss Webster*]: Yes. Mechanist seeks that which is without exception.

Royce: Isn't it a pragmatic requirement? Question of canonical form of laws of nature. Case of lunar theory: moon of theory and moon of experience never agree.

Troland: In biology Pearson, etc., study of correlation. Always statistical; it is a functional relation sought by a statistical method.

Brogan: "Cause" should be abolished. Responsibility, legal and moral. Theoretical [existence of] mechanisms and general laws without exceptions. Mechanistic science not in conflict with intention. Scientific and not emotional. "Omniscient tychism" [belongs] in mythical group. Freedom of will is of no importance except "freedom from non-intentional action." Second misconception: teleology. "If mechanism were a complete account" does conflict, [as does] "Science is special." [But] volition and teleology [are] both mistaken.

Royce: Need of greater freedom of theory. Chance means curve of chance. Cf. evolution of elements. Second law of energy is not mechanical; is it without exception?

Troland: Brownian movement exception to second law. Chance is always subject to limitations, e.g., by first law.

Dr. Van Riper: [Note.] Insists on knowing why. What is advantage of this, e.g., cause of eclipse? Social desire to know motives was first occasion of this. Not satisfied with external action. So in physical world. Can formulate an attitude. Why not say *control* nature? Causal terminology does not help control, but there is a subjective appeal of cause.

Royce: Apperceiving (Herbartian), not control?

Van Riper: More intimacy with world.

Royce: Hall's investigation of cause in legal affairs. There are responsibilities in business [that are] not penal, e.g., [those covered by] insurance. Maxim—Bacon: "Law is interested only in proximate cause." Responsible person might reasonably have foreseen—insurance, strict construction. Conceptions cross.

[Next] Troland, Brogan, defining question of criteria. Eliot, psychology.

March 10, 1914

ક્ક SUMMARY

Professor Royce first called attention to Henrich Weber's "classification theory" of causality. Then, in continuation of the discussion of the previous meeting, he said that the statistical view of nature, as held by Charles Peirce, presupposes the existence of finite collections of discrete individuals. Peirce's own views about continuity are not clear. Furthermore the statistical theory, at least in Peirce's development of it, conceived the reality of objective chance—that is, of events which, however far analyzed, would fall into the familiar bell curve of chance. But a tendency to eliminate chance was also present, so that fixed law now had rather the upper hand, but was not absolute.

The topic of the evening, "causality," was next entered upon in the form of short papers. The purpose of these papers was to answer constructively why it is people have sought for what they have called "causes" in various sciences.

Miss Webster began the discussion by a paper on "cause" in biology. She began by a brief review of uses of the causal concept. She criticized as unworkable the notion of cause as totality of antecedents, referred to the vagueness of the notion of invariable antecedent, and said the identification of cause with last-observed prior stage was often to call attention to something scientifically unimportant. She favored more the proposal to reduce causality to mathematical functional connections, and the proposal to bring cause into relation with the concept of probability. But an experimental science, for instance experimental biology, has a use for the term "cause" which has been formulated by Jennings in a way interestingly analogous to Mill's method of difference. It is, namely, that while you cannot find the cause for an event, you can find the cause for the difference between two events, the cause being a corresponding difference running through previous events. It is just the work of experimental science to find the causes for differences in the sense defined.

Mr. Troland offered the comment that the statistical search for causality was not necessarily contrasted with mathematical functional relationships. The study of correlations, for instance, is the search for a functional relationship by use of a statistical method.

A discussion followed between Professor Royce and Mr. Brogan as to whether the actual existence of mechanical laws which have no exceptions is postulated in advance by the scientist, or whether the scientist merely looks for laws as nearly without exception as possible, and for pragmatic reasons. This led to the reading of Mr. Brogan's paper, which was a defense of the rigid mechanistic conception in science. He first paid his respects to certain theories which he said he did not understand, and then added that the word "cause" might well be abolished from science, but that science does presuppose mechanisms and the existence of general laws to which there are no exceptions. Arguments against this are based on an appeal either to responsibility or to free will or to teleology. Legal responsibility is irrelevant here. Moral responsibility goes over into the problem of the freedom of the will; but the only sense in which ethics demands freedom is freedom from non-intentional action, that is, action not flowing from the normal functioning of the agent, and this sort of freedom is not at all opposed to mechanism. As regards teleology, there is always the philosophical possibility of holding that science is special and not the complete account; but for science itself theory and not emotion must prevail, and theory demands rigid law.

Professor Royce called for a greater freedom of theory than this mechanistic view admitted of. For instance, the second law of energy stands contrasted with the strictly mechanical, and also it is doubtful as to whether it does not admit of exceptions. Mr. Troland adduced the Brownian movements as a case in point, but urged that such exceptions were subject to very narrow limitations.

Dr. Van Riper read a paper wherein he held cause was in its origin similar to the social desire to know the motives of others. We are not satisfied in either case with the external action. Merely for control of nature, laws and equations would suffice, but men have, whether wisely or not, gone beyond this, and sought for a deeper intimacy with the world.

Professor Royce closed the evening's discussion by making some comments on the legal notion of cause and the conflicts of such a legal maxim as "The responsible person is the cause of any outcome of his action, however remote, which he might reasonably have foreseen," with the Baconian maxim "The law considers only proximate causes."

March 17, 1914

३► NOTES

[*Royce*]: Weber's account of cause: dependent on a classification of things; match, fire, death, diseases are classes of events.

Ursache:	a_1	a_2	a_3	a_4
Wirkung:	b_2	b_1	b_4	b_3

There is *some* one-one correspondence, of immediate sequence (immediate here means no interesting *betweens*). Whatever event happens, it belongs to a class of events which has a class of antecedents of this sort. No discoverable rule in all cases. Cases; conflagrations, etc. Try to make the classes as simple as possible. If they are so simple that the class has a very simple name, we have a law of nature. Need not be mechanical causation. If your two classes were unit-classes, every consequent would have a determinate antecedent, but a larger simple class is better. If a simple class of effects has a complex class of antecedents, then we say this is "accidental."

Costello: Verbal "simples"? Prediction? Arbitrary classes?

Royce to Van Riper: No rule of cause need be defined.

Eliot: [Note] read by Sen Gupta. Cause, etc., can be explained away and not explained. Can we do without superstition? *"Participation"*—Lévy-Bruhl; any attribution of force or volition is participation. Double participation is cause: cause-effect and object-us. Will is internal. We have no direct knowledge of will, but [rather] it is an ideal construction. Volition and cause become distinguished, i.e., two sorts of participation separated. Cause means invariable events. [To the] primitive, [there is] no mere fact and [there is] no mere idea. Necessity and chance, etc., are hypothetical. [Their] inevitable appearance.

Royce: Logically useless and logically inevitable. A construction.

Brogan: Contrast with Münsterberg.

Royce: Stout and Ward's controversy with Royce. Experience of activity is primal: "stream of consciousness" feels its own course. The feeling of activity and fulfillment does appear in consciousness. But is our notion of causality here derived? Do we pre-know what the result will be? Humean analysis: could we form a generalization? A law? James on experience of activity.

Sen Gupta: [Note.] We need an ideal constructed whole before we can say a single fact causes another. This is true of all causes. Time irrelevant. Mutual determination. What use [has causality]? —hypothesis, action, socialization of knowledge.

Royce: Entirely a conception with a practical use?

Sen Gupta: No, not merely, but semi-subjective.

Royce: Question: Why more interesting to find sequences than coexistences? Why not laws of coexistence? There are in geometry, but not in physics.

Headley: [Note.] Of Aristotle's four causes, *material* [cause is] neglected; *formal* is equal to *final*—what is to be. *Final* not scientific; and "end effect" is a confusion of two sorts: goodness of end, and purpose, [which] equals efficient cause. *Efficient,* meaning mechanical, cause remains. Still confused—psychological. But practical use finds Locke and Hume and Bosanquet irrelevant. [Causality is] never a mere logical relationship; [it is] temporal and dynamic. Volition irrelevant. Relation of cause [to] effect is not simple. Wundt [classifies cause as] (1) thing, (2) force, (3) regular connected processes. Second not really apart from third. All three used as we are interested; variety of motives; we choose the particular cause. Two scientists may offer two distinct accounts, both true. What is significant? Not proximity, but interest owing to exceptional character. May classify sciences by the notion of cause which they use.

Costello: What is interest?

Miss Webster: Depends on choice of events you compare an event with.

Royce: Interest is objective in being determined by environment. You compare with certain other events.

Miss Webster: Depends on the context of the interesting objects. Not especially realistic, not subjective; but there is comparison.

Brogan: Aristotle's causes: correlation. Aristotle a binding, a correlation. Four significant ways of binding [something] with something else.

Brogan next time: reduce all value terms to one.

March 17, 1914

ह्ल SUMMARY

Professor Royce, at the beginning of the meeting, summarized Heinrich Weber's proposal of a generalized concept of cause. Given an event, it can always be put into a class W $\lfloor Wirkung \rfloor$ of events such that there is another class U $[Ursache]$ of events which can be correlated with the class W by a one-one relation, that relation being the relation of "a predecessor with no interesting intermediaries." To say every event has a cause is to say no more than that every event belongs to a class of events which has a class of antecedents of this sort. As thus generalized, the concept of cause is of little use unless the classes in question have a class-concept which is simple. In such a case we have a "law of nature." If a simple class of consequents have a class of antecedents which have no simple defining concept, the events are said to happen accidentally.

Dr. Costello asked whether the classes chosen were arbitrary, and whether the notion of a class with a simple name did not stand in need of a further criterion of simplicity. The answer to these questions was in the affirmative.

Mr. Eliot's paper on causality was then read by Mr. Sen Gupta. Causality is something which can be explained away but not explained. Perhaps it is due to superstition, but can we do without such superstitions? Many such notions arise through what Lévy-Bruhl has called, in his work on primitive race-psychology, the "law of participation." Indeed causality is, in the first instance, due to a double process of participation, that between effect and cause and that between the object and us. Later these two sorts of participation get separated into cause and volition, invariable sequence and act of will. But both are ideal constructs, inevitable yet fictitious.

Mr. Brogan contrasted this view with that of Professor Münsterberg, which conceives the immediate life experience with its volitions and values as real, and its connections to be of meaning and not of cause; and the causal world of matter an inevitable but nevertheless artificial postulate. Professor Royce recalled a controversy he had had with Stout and Ward as to the place the feeling our own activity had in the genesis of the concept of causal law. Professor Royce accepted the conclusions of Hume so far as to hold that no prediction nor any formulation of general law could ever result from the mere feeling of our own activity.

Mr. Sen Gupta next read his own paper, wherein he upheld a view similar to that of Bosanquet, that the only true notion of cause is that of mutual determination within an ideal constructed whole. The uses of causality are for verification, for action, and for the socialization of knowledge.

Professor Royce asked if Mr. Sen Gupta held that cause was a concept for practical use only. The reply was that it was not, but was, nevertheless, semi-subjective. Professor Royce incidentally raised the question why in physical science laws of sequence are more obtainable and more interesting than are laws of coexistence.

Mr. Headley then read the last of the papers on causality. Of Aristotle's four causes only efficient cause remains, and that in an altered form. Mr. Headley held that causality was not a simple relation nor was it a merely logical one, but was temporal and dynamic if anything. Wundt classes types of cause as (1) things, (2) forces, (3) regular connected processes. We use one or another of these notions just as our interest demands, and you might classify the sciences according to their notion of causes. Two scientists might give totally different accounts of the cause of an event, and both be right—the direction of their interest differing.

Dr. Costello called for a definition of "interest" which should prevent Mr. Headley's account from being circular. Miss Webster said the difference of interest was the difference in the sort of events you compared the given event with. Mr. Brogan added the comment that Aristotle's causes are really modes of correlation: they are the four significant ways of binding something with something else.

Comment: Our discussion of cause has brought out two ways of considering causality which seem to me to be of the widest scientific importance: first, the way of reducing cause to invariable sequence —or, since this formulation suggests "same cause, same effect," that is, that identical causes recur, and this notion is probably false since perhaps the same causes never do recur, we had best state this first notion of cause as that of mathematical functional connection, a law of nature; second, the way such as is indicated in Miss Webster's view of cause as the experimentally discoverable cause for the difference between two phenomena. The former treats the causal relation in extension: the members of a certain class of causes are severally followed by the members of a certain class of effects, and this fact can be stated in a universal proposition. The second treats the relation rather in intension, and could be studied in, perhaps not indeed the single case, but in a very small group of cases. The first is enumerative, the second analytic. I wish to call attention to this distinction, because I think the second sort of causality, of which Miss Webster's case of the cause of a difference is a very typical example, is frequently neglected by those who hurry to reduce cause to law. This sort of causality-analysis gives you a law by first giving you something in the way of a reason for the law; and since we can never examine all the possible cases, unless the law can be established by showing a reason more ultimate than the law itself, no law of nature is ever empirically verifiable. The case of choosing fair samples and thus rendering the law probable does not contradict what has just been said, for what you do in sampling is to select your samples under diverse conditions, and thus really perform an analysis which shows that these conditions are more or less irrelevant, by the method of agreement. I do not have time here to expand these remarks far enough to do justice to the subject; I simply wish to indicate certain considerations which the discussion of the last two meetings has impressed upon me.

March 24, 1914

৯৬ NOTES

Brogan's paper: [42] Definition and implication in value propositions. Exclude extrinsic value; not discuss reductions of value to psychological terms, etc. Value propositions either ultimately analyze into non-value terms or not. First move: to reduce all to one value term. G. E. Moore takes "good"; he has never defined "bad" (intrinsically); can't infer notion of "better" (capability of de-

---

[42]   Brogan recalls that this was not a formal paper but a presentation from notes, with formulae written on the blackboard. His remarks were drawn from a preliminary draft of his doctoral dissertation, completed in May, 1914. Cf. A. P. Brogan, "The Logical Analysis of Intrinsic Value" (abstract of a paper read before the American Philosophical Association, December, 1914), *Journal of Philosophy*, XII (February 18, 1915), 105–06, and the *Philosophical Review*, XXIV (March, 1915), 196–97; "The Fundamental Value Universal," *Journal of Philosophy*, XVI (February 13, 1919), 96–104. Cf. *A Philosophy of the Real and the Possible*, p. 119.

grees).[43] [But] good is better than bad; existence of good is better than non-existence: we ought to pursue the good, a priori.[44]

The existence of A is better than or is worse than or equals the non-existence of A.

The existence of A is better than or is worse than or equals the existence of B.

A is neither good nor bad when the existence of A equals the non-existence of A.

Intrinsically good existence of A is better than non-existence of A.

Intrinsically bad existence of A is worse than non-existence of A.

A is best means no other possibility equal or better (of a group).

A ought to be done means A is the best possible. (*Royce:* No *sum* of goods.)

A ought not to be done means there is another, B, better than A. ("Conduces to" is an extrinsic value.)

[*Brogan* on aesthetic values]: Beauty solves Kant's antinomies of *Geschmacksurteil,* [the] individual and [the] universal. A judgment of beauty gives one's own personal reaction, but not that merely—[it] is really a joint assertion.

A is beautiful means I enjoy A and any subject's-enjoying-A is greatly of intrinsic good.

[*?Royce*]: What is aesthetic enjoyment?

Brogan: Isolating. Not bodily. Sunk in objects—empathy. Take any case.

A is not beautiful means I do not enjoy it or some subject's-enjoying-A is not greatly of intrinsic good.

Eliot: Aesthetic enjoyment means A *is* beautiful.

[After discussion of the point, the definition] "If any subject en-

---

[43] Cf. Brogan, *Journal of Philosophy,* XVI, 99.

[44] At this point and again at the beginning of the March 31 notes, Costello listed Brogan's symbols for the primitive ideas "better than" ($\gtrless$) and "worse than" ($\lessgtr$), considered as transitive asymmetrical relations, and for "equals," "the existence of A," and "the non-existence of A." At Brogan's suggestion the editor has substituted verbal equivalents for the symbols in these notes.

joys A, subject's-enjoying-A is not [greatly of] intrinsic good"
[was] rejected.

Brogan: Taking *better* as fundamental; *best,* for definition of
others. [On non-existence]: Non-existence is equal, neutral, value.
The existence of A is better than or equals or is worse than the existence of B. Assume [that] the existence of A is worse than the
existence of B: the non-existence of A equals the non-existence of
B.[45]

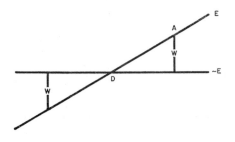

The existence of A plus the existence of B is better than the existence of A. [The problem of] Moore's principle of organic unity;
the existence of A plus the existence of B equals the existence of C,

45   The editor interprets the illustrating diagram as follows: Oblique line E
represents the locus of existences; horizontal line ~E, the locus of non-exist-
ences; vertical W above or below ~E, intrinsic goodness or badness; point A,
any existence intrinsically good or bad. Point D, the intersection, seems to
represent an existence neither good nor bad and therefore equal in value to a
non-existence. "Better" or "worse" may be predicated of A and of D (the direction in which the symbol "W" is turned having no significance here), but
everything on ~E is of equal value; i.e., non-existence is indifferent. The diagram may be thought of as a two-dimensional model to be manipulated: if E
is rotated with D as a pivot, it can be made to coincide with ~E, in which
event W,W will disappear and all points on E will acquire the neutral value of
corresponding points on ~E. One of the existence points might be labeled "B."

[but there is] no logical inference [that] the existence of AB equals the existence of C.

Anything better than D [cf. diagram] is intrinsically good. No *measurement* as yet, no unit.

[*Costello* in manuscript]: Does "plus" differ from "and" as above used?

March 24, 1914
ह‌े SUMMARY

Mr. Brogan presented a sketch of a possible reduction, by the aid of symbols, of all value terms to one value term, so that one could, in discussing the relation of values to other entities, do so by considering the relation simply of this single fundamental value term to those other entities, and thus make the problem more definite. Mr. Brogan excluded from discussion the so-called extrinsic or instrumental values, and, for the present, the reduction of values to anything not a value. He held that "good" [46] cannot be taken, as G. E. Moore does, as the central value term, for by means of it one can define neither "bad" nor "better." Nor can one, by using it, establish in any way except that of merely postulating them as true, such propositions as: "Good is better than bad," "The existence of good is better than its non-existence," or "We ought to pursue the good."

But taking "better," considered as a transitive [a]symmetrical relation, as the primitive idea, then all other value terms fall into place. One must also assume various non-valuational concepts, etc., for instance, "the existence of" an object. Then in turn we may define: "worse," "equal in value," "of indifferent value," "intrin-

---

[46] Costello wrote " 'the good' "; the emendation is suggested by Brogan.

sically good," "intrinsically bad," "best," "ought to be done," etc.

Mr. Brogan next proposed definitions of "beautiful," "not beautiful" and "ugly," which raised considerable criticism, since the definition of "not beautiful" which was proposed was not the contradictory of the definition of "beautiful." Also there was dispute as to whether "aesthetic enjoyment" could be given a non-valuational psychological definition.

Mr. Brogan then proposed as an axiom that all non-existent entities be considered equal in value, which, along with the definition of intrinsically good, sufficed to make their value null. Another discussion then followed as to, supposing the existence of A is valuable and so also the existence of B, whether then the existence of both is more valuable than the existence of only one. Mr. Brogan held this was axiomatic, except in the case of organic unity, where one value influenced another. (This point needed further explanation.)

March 31, 1914

৯৯ NOTES

[*Brogan's paper continued.*]

A is beautiful means I enjoy A, and some subject's-enjoying-A is good. Df.

A is not beautiful means I don't enjoy A, or no subject's-enjoying-A is good. Df.

A is better than B means the existence of A is better than the existence of B. Df.[47]

A is intrinsically good means the existence of A is better than the non-existence of A. Df.

---

[47] Brogan says that this should be followed by the definition: "A is worse than B = B is better than A."

A is intrinsically bad means the existence of A is worse than the non-existence of A. Df.

Aesthetic postulates: relation p $\supset$ q, etc.[48]

If one enjoyment of A is good, any enjoyment is good.

If one enjoyment of A is not good, no enjoyment is good.

A is more beautiful than B means A, B, are beautiful, and some enjoyment of A better.

A is not more beautiful than B means A, B, are not beautiful, or no enjoyment of A better. (*Royce* suggests: A, at least, is beautiful.)

A is ugly: inference, [A is] not beautiful. And, A is beautiful: inference, A is not ugly.

A is ugly means I dislike A, and all enjoyment [of A] is bad.

[Discussion]:

[*Brogan*]: Seldom any comparison in aesthetics.

Royce objects: Is there no highest beauty? We say often this is perfect, as it ought to be.[49]

[*Brogan*]: Aesthetic experience is not a comparison [of works of art as objects].

Eliot: Compact series?

[*Brogan*]· Doubtful.

Blake: "I don't like that, but it is beautiful, I know."

[*Brogan*]: Not a true aesthetic judgment; [rather] "this is considered beautiful." More personal [i.e., a matter of experience. The definition of beauty I propose recalls the] impressionists in France [in its] first half, dogmatists [in only] the second [half].

Royce: Better to go into series and develop all possibilities and various ways in which they might be objective. Not mathematically, but for use. Better to be far in advance: e.g., in intensive quantities, hard/soft, A dents or scratches B.

[*Brogan*]: One enjoyment might be better than another—not uniquely determined by the object.

48 Brogan describes these postulates as confused and as mostly not his.
49 It is not clear from the manuscript whether this sentence should be attributed to Royce or to Brogan.

Royce: History of causes of works of art.

Woods: Want a scale for judging critics; much more exactness needed than in enjoyment. Could measure, e.g., Italian masters, madonnas. Could analyze parts of the object.

[*Brogan*]: Two factors, art and natural object, in every painting —Lalo [*Introduction à l'esthétique*].

Woods: Isn't beauty due to biological causes?

[*?Brogan*]: No one has any true artistic sense who doesn't feel the *making* of it is good. Once it was usefulness.

[*Brogan*]: Definition of aesthetic experience: "I take delight in the contemplation of A."

Eliot calls for more.

Hefelbower: "Delight in revenge."

[*Brogan* on moral value]: Truth not a value. Freedom, etc., used in eulogistic sense, are not themselves value terms.

Scale: trouble with "equality." The existence of A equals the existence of B; the existence of B equals the existence of C: inference, the existence of A equals the existence of C. Pp.[50]

Royce on symmetry?

[*Brogan*]: Summation (assuming no organic unity): the existence of A and the existence of B [are] better than the existence of A, all being intrinsically good. The existence of A equals the non-existence of A: inference, the existence of A and the existence of B equal the existence of B. Etc. Unit of value arbitrary, fairly low, G_1. The existence of G_1 is better than the non-existence of G_1. X equals G_1: the existence of G_1 and the existence of X equal the existence of G_2. Say G_2 is twice G_1. So also for bad, B_1, when the existence of B_1 and the existence of G_1 equal the non-existence of G_1. Might interpolate fractions; might define, subtract. The existence of G_2 and the existence of B_1 equal the existence of G_1.

Royce: Associative, etc., character? Formal defects, e.g., in equality. Quantity, however, is a luxury; needs proof of associative law of addition, etc. Non-associative, no group. If an act has three re-

[50] This proposition may have been stated by Royce; the manuscript is again unclear.

sults, one bad, you need to evaluate the whole. Proof of distributive character of addition and multiplication has demanded great work: Russell, Huntington (multiplication and addition), E. B. Wilson (technique). Hamilton's quaternions, commutative multiplication impossible.

Woods: Extrinsic good?

Troland: Why not "good for"? Need to be analyzed.

Royce: "Better" preferable to "good." Every argument against objectivity fallacious.

Next: Troland, quanta.

March 31, 1914
ટ≫ SUMMARY

Mr. Brogan continued his discussion of the reduction of various values to the central value concept of "better." He first reviewed his previous discussion and proposed a revision of his former definition of "beautiful." "A is beautiful" shall mean, "I enjoy A, and some enjoyment of A is good." He proposed in addition the postulate, "If some enjoyment of A is good, all enjoyments of A are good." He then defined "A is more beautiful than B," "A is ugly," etc. A discussion followed, in which it was inquired whether you could compare, as to beauty, a symphony with a painting. Mr. Blake objected to the first clause of the definition of beauty, citing such expressions as: "I don't like this, but it is beautiful, I know." Mr. Brogan replied that such an expression was equivalent to "This is considered beautiful," and was not itself a true aesthetic judgment. He preferred his own definition, as uniting in one the impressionist and dogmatist definitions of beauty. Mr. Brogan then replied to a query as to the use of the word "enjoy" in the proposed definition, defining aesthetic enjoyment as "I take delight in the contemplation of A." Messrs. Eliot and Hefelbower objected to the adequacy of this, the latter citing "delight in revenge" as a non-aesthetic contemplation.

A remark by Mr. Brogan that he wished to develop his theory only so far as it could be applied, led Professor Royce to insist on the great value of developing any theory fully, since one never knew what applications might arise. Dr. Woods supported the same view, and further asked if it was not possible to get other criteria of beauty. The discussion of other topics followed, among them the problem of aesthetic origins, the relation of beauty to activities of making, the question as to what constitutes natural beauty, etc.

Mr. Brogan then continued his discussion of other sorts of value. He eliminated the problems of the value of truth, freedom, and the like. There was some discussion of extrinsic and instrumental values. But most of the time was taken up with the endeavor to formulate a value series, the chief problem being to secure connexity in the series. Mr. Brogan was unable, as yet, to prove equality in value to be a symmetrical transitive relation.[51] Also he had not secured the associative character of his proposed operation of value addition. Prof. Royce cited other examples of similar difficulties, and warned against introducing by postulates anything that could be proved otherwise.

April 7, 1914

ᏹ NOTES

Brogan [Basic postulates]:
[1.1] Better is contained in diversity.

51   Brogan writes to the editor: "I do not remember about 'equality in value.' Then or later I 'defined' it: A is equal in value to B = A is neither better nor worse than B. Df. (Where 'not better' was limited to what is in the 'field' of better or worse.)"

[1.2] Better is transitive.

[1.3] The relation product of better and not worse is contained in better.[52]

Royce: Great difficulty of building up postulate sets: parallel-line postulate; distributive character of operations of ∩ and ∪ hard to establish, new postulate needed. Schröder, Kempe, Royce.

[On] Woods and Cattell; eugenics engaged in hopeless controversy. Pearson and Mendelians.

Troland: [Paper.] [53] Statistical mechanics; quanta. Peirce's views [e.g., in "The Architecture of Theories"]. Modern physics reveals large fields of statistical relationships. [Statistical method] hypothetical: does not average individuals but *assumes* individuals, applies probability, deduces, tests by experimental measurements. Assumes a discontinuous, atomistic universe. Hence atomism supports probability theory. Heat as molecular motion; chemical atom. Since 1898 electrical phenomena seem atomistic, negative and probably positive also. Molecules, atoms, electrons. Most modern theory of radiation as atomistic; wave theory doubtful. Bunches or "chunks" of energy—units of radiation: light quanta. Planck, 1904(?) [i.e., 1900]. Quanta can be treated only statistically.

Maxwell showed that a large number of molecules at random speeds [conformed to] a bell curve. (1) Evaporation increases logarithmically with temperature. (2) Second law of thermodynamics (uniform distribution of heat). (3) Brownian movement—Perrin. (4) Thermo-electric effect. Metals contain free electrons;

---

[52] The manuscript uses symbolic notation for the above postulates; the verbal equivalents have been supplied to the editor by Brogan, who adds the following explanations:

1.1. "That is, if A is better than B, then A is not (exactly) identical with B."

1.2. "That is, if A is better than B, and B is better than C, then A is better than C."

1.3. "That is, if A is better than B and B is not worse than C, then A is better than C."

[53] Cf. D. F. Comstock and L. T. Troland, *The Nature of Matter and Electricity* (New York, 1917), pp. 182–89; and for the probable sources of Troland's material, *ibid.*, p. 189.

some move fast enough to escape from the metal; [rate] increases with heat, [in a] bell curve [with respect to] number and velocity. (5) In chemistry, law of chemical mass-action, deduced from random distribution of atoms. Law is: "Rate of chemical reaction is proportional to concentration of reagents" (bimolecular proportional to square). (6) Constitution of atom; radioactivity. Life of a radioactive substance and speed of radiated particles logarithmic like evaporation.

History of radiation-quanta theory. (1) Radiation has an analogy to bell curve.[54] Hence intensity of radiation dependent on velocities. Difficulty of deducing a law on wave theory of continuous radiation. Max Planck assumed radiation not continuous. Then an equation fitted the empirical curve (1902). Proved fruitful in other fields. (2) Photo-electric effect. When light strikes a metal surface, electrons are emitted, independent in speed of intensity of light but fewer in number. (Amount of energy in quantum is inversely proportional to wave length; photo-electric effect bears out; so X rays.) (3) Specific heats not constant for low temperatures; near absolute zero, approached zero; no specific heat at zero degrees. Quantum theory applied by Nernst and Einstein. (4) Energy atomistic. Magnetism. Can be magnetized to intensities 1, 2, 3, etc. Energy stored up must be a multiple. (5) Theory of constitution of hydrogen atom. Spectrum lines calculated by simple formula. [In] 1913, a hypothesis: one positive nucleus plus one electron. Deduced formula. [Conclusion]: energy is atomistic. Changes and transfers of energy in bundles. Events are atomistic, therefore.

In how far is physical universe statistical? Very largely, but not all. Possible classification: (1) laws statistically determined, (2) statistically blurred, (3) non-statistical. (1) Second law. Down-hill movement of heat more probable. Entropy tends to a maximum and is a function of probability. Evaporation curves, including radiation. (2) Chemical mass-action. Uniformity of temperature; i.e., total average is near a level, depends on conservation of energy; but

---

54 The manuscript includes a simple diagram illustrating this analogy.

when we take a large number, then individuality is eliminated. No surface uniformly illuminated, but uniform in the main. (3) Conservation of energy; energy proportional to frequency, which quantum theory is itself founded on. Determining factor is non-statistical in a bell curve, i.e., where the maximum is.

Probability of exceptions to statistical laws. Brownian movement reverses second law [of energy].

Royce: Good to get such summaries.

Brogan: [Discussion of] aesthetic judgments and theoretical judgments on aesthetic values. (Second half [of the evening].)

Royce: Old *Saturday Review* used to make two estimates of politics, one dispassionate, the other not; middle 'seventies. Short period in *Nation.* In art [a double estimate is] valuable at times.

Discussion of beauty-judgment and theoretical aesthetic judgment.

Royce: Russell's first lecture had *"harte Schönheit"*—[phrase from] Schröder. Hocking formerly interested in elegance of mathematical demonstration; not adaptation exactly of skill of thinker.[55] Schröder is mixture of sloppy and *gemütlich.* Peirce misses it [sc. elegance] along with power of exposition. Not get beauty by polemics.

April 7, 1914

ঌ SUMMARY

The meeting was chiefly devoted to two topics, the one a continuation of the discussion of Mr. Brogan's symbolism for a theory of value, the other a paper by Mr. Troland on "Statistical Mechanics."

[55] W. E. Hocking was active in the seminar of 1901–02. According to Royce's notes for October 22, 1901, Hocking, in discussing "what constitutes elegance in demonstration," found the main element to be "naturalness."

In the former, Mr. Brogan restated again his fundamental postulates for securing a serial order among values, and admitted he was still unable to establish the transitivity of his relation of equality among values. Professor Royce rehearsed some of his own trials and troubles with the formulation of sets of postulates. He referred, also, to the familiar difficulties with the Euclidean parallel postulate, and to Schröder's labors in the endeavor to prove the distributive character of the operations of logical multiplication and addition.

Later in the evening there was a discussion of Mr. Brogan's contrast between aesthetic judgments, which require personal enjoyment, and purely theoretical judgments about the beauty of something one does not oneself enjoy. Professor Royce referred to the *Saturday Review* of the middle 'seventies, which carried on two parallel estimates of current politics, one partisan, the other entirely dispassionate. This discussion led to one concerning the beauty of abstract theories themselves. Professor Royce referred to Professor Hocking's former inquiries into what constitutes "elegance" in mathematical demonstrations. This quality cannot be reduced simply to terms of "adaptation." Mr. B. Russell's first Lowell Lecture was quoted as an example of a simple presentation which, by reason of that very fact, had a certain *"harte Schönheit."* The last phrase is from Schröder, who, though appreciating such qualities in others, was himself a mixture of the sloppy and the *gemütlich.*

Mr. Troland's paper on "Statistical Mechanics" began by saying there are large fields in modern physics where the most effective method is the employment of statistics. Such a method assumes a discontinuous atomistic universe. It does not take averages of given individuals, but deduces probabilities about hypothetical individuals, and tests by experimental measurement. The present trend towards atomism is favorable to the use of probability, for atoms can seldom be effectively studied in any other way. The chemical atom and the molecular theory of heat are both of comparatively long standing. Since 1898 the atomistic interpretation of electrical phenomena has become widely accepted. And lastly, the most modern theory of radiation, Planck's theory of light quanta, is atomistic.

There are numerous empirical phenomena which seem to conform to the familiar bell curve of chance, for instance (1) evaporation, (2) the second law of thermodynamics, (3) the Brownian movement, (4) the thermo-electric effect, (5) the law of chemical mass-action, (6) radioactivity.

Mr. Troland then traced briefly the empirical evidence for Planck's quantum theory, mentioning (1) the nature of the curve of intensity of radiation, (2) the photo-electric effect, (3) specific heats for low temperatures, (4) discontinuity of increases in magnetism, (5) the theory of the hydrogen spectrum and corresponding hydrogen atom. The conclusion seems to be that energy is atomistic, and since it is, therefore, transferred in bundles, events are atomistic.

Lastly, Mr. Troland inquired into the possible extent of statistical methods, and held their scope was very wide in physical science, but not all-embracing. He said there were laws (1) statistically determined, (2) statistically blurred, and (3) non-statistical. Among (1) laws statistically determined are the second law of thermodynamics, the laws of evaporation, etc. These seem almost entirely statistical. (2) A case of statistical blurring is that of apparent uniform temperature, or, again, that of apparent uniform illumination. (3) As an example of a non-statistical law, the first law of thermodynamics was adduced. Also, the place of the maximum of a bell curve is not statistically determined.

The paper was not followed by discussion!

April 14, 1914

᨞ NOTES

Southard: Value of negative cases in "Significance of Bacteria in a Cadaver." [56] How prove these produce no effect? Especially when taken in a group. If they are effective, may cause obscure diseases.

Royce: Many cases where no bacteria come in.

Southard: Riches of result. Mental not the same as physical, hence diet of insane same as diet of sane. Investigated kidney (one thousand cases): 70% had severe kidney disease. One hundred random cases microscopically: every case! Kidney disease (100%) more frequent in insane than brain disease (90%). Possible objections; 63% brain, 70% kidney. Liver, spleen, heart; [of] cases with severe kidney disease (thirty-three cases) twenty-seven [had] severe brain [disease], ten to twelve [disease] of liver, etc. Common symptom depression—kidney phenomena; brain filled with metabolic clogging materials in depression cases; 100% embarrassed.

Royce: Entirely uniform, therefore doubtful.

Southard: Lady gave money to study relation of environment to insanity [with stipulation that it was] necessary to prove normal brains! High [standard of] technique gives [diagnosis of] brain

[56] Cf. F. P. Gay and E. E. Southard, "The Significance of Bacteria Cultivated from the Human Cadaver: A Study of One Hundred Cases of Mental Disease," *Centralblatt für Bakteriologie*, LV (June 24, 1910), 117–33; Southard and Myrtelle M. Canavan, "On the Nature and Importance of Kidney Lesions in Psychopathic Subjects: A Study of One Hundred Cases Autopsied at the Boston State Hospital," *Journal of Medical Research*, XXXI (November, 1914), 285–99; Canavan and Southard, "The Significance of Bacteria Cultivated from the Human Cadaver: A Second Series of One Hundred Cases of Mental Disease," *Journal of Medical Research*, XXXI (January, 1915), 339–65.

disease. Hyperkinesis (mania, etc.) most consistent with normality
of brain. Over-activity goes with normal brain—intrinsically normal, extrinsically abnormal. Start with motor phenomena and go
back, neuron by neuron, and find each neuron normal; whole brain
maybe normal. Other organs may excite brain; perhaps "ideas"!
Opponent says, "Brain disease of a functional character." Metaphysical theory of identity; or an Ostwald-like biotic energy
(rather naïve, combining structural and functional).

Royce: Dangerously commonplace, you say.

Southard: You come out with a truism.

Royce: Like Spencer's "rhythm of motion." Did not notice
Fourier's series.

Southard: Spencer's inner and outer relations in harmony not
very profound.

Woods: All statistics are of this sort; not a startling discovery.

Southard: Abnormal vs. morbid. Academic students expect disease to be supernormal or subnormal in a quantitative way: ano-
mality. Pathological point of view says disease does or does not destroy a cell—survival value, negative cases, all or nothing. (*Psychological Bulletin* [and] paper at New Haven.) [57] Delusions
(paranoid) turn out *motor*—*Aufgabe*-Würzburg. Catalepsy, epilepsy, etc., are *sensory*! Need normal muscles. It is what you do
with the ideas that counts. What is a thing when it is entirely different from what it is? (1) Originality: guess there is something
and then look for it—interpolation, statistical series built up. (2)
Deny something: this is pathological method—take out liver and
see what happens. Fallacy of making negative into positive: "significance of *un* in *unconscious*." Hypostatized a novel kind of conscious; Peirce, *subconscious* (normal), *co-conscious* (new). Does
consciousness have degrees? Early workers used *mind* in vague
sense. Then introspectionists: consciousness perhaps *self-conscious-
ness*. Then consciousness equated with *ideas*, etc., and technique for

[57] Southard, *Psychological Bulletin*, XI, 117–30; *ibid.*, pp. 66–67. With the remarks following, cf. his "Considerations Bearing on the Seat of Consciousness,"
Journal of Nervous and Mental Disease, XLI (September, 1914), 581.

finding. Consciousness is *Bewusstsein,* cognition; not will and emotions, which come in by kinaesthetic. Does will ever get to consciousness? Frontal lobes destroyed without loss of cognition. Parietal lesions did destroy consciousness. Mind is more than consciousness (history); but making of events is elsewhere. Behaviorist considers frontal lobe; introspector considers back part. Psychologist must be both.

Royce: Abnormal vs. morbid. Normal means average. Quételet thought the average was the desirable. Morbid means absence of certain functions, etc.

Southard: Tumor paranoia [symptoms are] lawless, unrestrained —excess. If academic student saw the bell curve and the abnormal at the end, it wouldn't be bad. Morbid has new curve.

Royce: Abnormal not bad.

Southard: Morbid is biological, pathological; abnormal [is] physical and logical. Pathology used to be considered by me as a heap of sciences. Pathology has now the all-or-nothing concept.

Royce: Notion of *non-*. Similar distinction of conscious and unconscious, etc. "Unconscious" did not enter through "introspection," but in transition from Descartes to Leibniz, in seventeenth-century psychology. Innate-idea discussion in Locke: mind lives to know itself. Notion of transition from potential to actual self-knowledge—knowing reflectively that one knows it. All ethical writers face it. In Leibniz another *reason:* not physiology, but relation of mind to objects. Roaring of sea. *Petites perceptions* not apperceived. Herbart held mind only accidentally conscious. James and Peirce referred to *co-conscious,* as if it belonged to some other mind.

Southard: What if Leibniz had used statistics?

Costello: Normal vs. average. Accidental.

Southard: Normative science quantitative?—Psychopathology awaits its Columbus (—Titchener). But the norms were not settled.

Royce: Normal or average not the valuable necessarily. Normal not purely statistical, as Woods has pointed out. The *great* are few, if tested by effects on destiny.

Woods: Wrong to speak of "humanity." If there were only humanity, then we should be interested in differences, should study each genealogical tree separately. No all or nothing; but series and "preservation of form."

Southard: Unformed and deformed, etc. New "model" idea: "preservation of form." Yes-no does not equal plus-minus. Does telephone work or not?—[the] quantitative may not be the important.

April 14, 1914

ᔰ SUMMARY

The meeting was devoted to the discussion by Professor Southard of various topics, for the most part bearing on the use of statistics. The first topic was the problem presented by the existence of certain bacteria in a cadaver. Some say it is a matter of course that these come in somehow after death. But the negative cases, where no bacteria are found, seem to demand a more special explanation. Another case was that of statistics which showed kidney disease more frequent in the insane than brain disease. Dr. Southard wondered if these statistics did not present too great a correlation, and whether possibly the kidney disease had no more to do with the matter than any other uniformly present concomitant, like the law of gravitation. It was possible, however, to suppose a real connection between mental depression in the insane and defective functioning of the kidneys. A third case was the problem arising when a lady gave money for the study of the relation of environment to insanity, which money was not to be used for cases where there was brain disease. The puzzle arose whether there were such cases. Though careful technique reveals brain disease in the larger number of cases, it may be there are cases where the whole brain is

intrinsically normal but is affected from without in such a way
as may produce, for example, over-activity. Dr. Southard expressed
a wish for a more adequate philosophical theory of mind and matter as a working basis for psychopathology. He added a further
point that some of his most elaborate researches had led to results
which anyone might have guessed at in the beginning. (Some discussion here intervened as to whether commonplace statistical results represent an advance in knowledge.)

Professor Southard then went on to contrast the abnormal and
the morbid. Abnormality is a sort of quantitative thing, a more or
less. But with the diseased, the morbid, the question is life or death,
yes or no, and there is a sharp contrast. Professor Southard said
there were two ways in which an investigator might be original:
one is to guess that something exists and then look for it, the other
is to inquire what would happen if something which does exist did
not exist. The latter is more the method of pathology. But it is a
great fallacy to try to make a negative into something positive.
That is what has too often happened with the notion of the *unconscious*, which has gotten hypostatized into a novel kind of conscious.
In Professor Southard's own inquiries concerning the bounds of
consciousness, he has seemed to find *mind* larger in scope than
consciousness, will and activity apparently falling outside. The
motor centers seem to be forward in the frontal lobe and their activity to be largely unaccompanied by consciousness; the seat of
that which introspection can reach is situated further back. The
conscious life that introspection reaches is history; the making
of events goes on elsewhere. Various paradoxes arise: for instance
delusions and fixed ideas turn out motor; catalepsy and epilepsy
turn out to be sensory.

Professor Royce then traced the development of the concept of
the unconscious in the history of philosophy, with special reference
to the "little perceptions" of Leibniz.

Another discussion turned on the distinction between the abnormal and the morbid. Professor Royce identified normal with
the average of a group, and critically referred to Quételet's at-

tempted identification of the normal with the desirable. Professor
Southard said he no longer considered pathology to be a heap of
sciences, but to have a leading idea of its own, the all-or-nothing
concept of the morbid. He asked if Professor Royce thought the
normative sciences quantitative studies of statistical averages. Professor Royce replied that that use of the term norm was a different
matter. Dr. Costello asked if the normal might not be contrasted
with the accidental, while the average was contrasted rather with
the unusual. But Professor Royce maintained that both were identical because both were statistics about groups. Dr. Costello replied,
the question of the normal was not to be evaded by saying the normal men were the group whose age at death averaged threescore
and ten. You may find normal men do average thus but first you
have to select your normal men, and the selecting of the class you
are going to average is not itself an average. Dr. Woods objected to
the all-or-nothing concept of the morbid, and preferred to contrast
the pathological with some notion of "preservation of form" which
would admit of degrees. Dr. Southard maintained his previous
position: in pathology the quantitative more or less is not the important notion, for in the biological world the organisms are unities, and like a telephone they will either work or not work, and
there is no half-way station.

Comment: I should like to state my opinions on two points, one
preliminary to the other. The preliminary one is the relation of
mathematical systems to systems in general, the other to which
this leads up, the concept of what I shall call systematic probability.

Mr. B. Russell maintains that all systematic connection is formal
logical connection; that all science reduces to two parts, the one
mathematics, which is the science of these formal connections, the
other, the replacing of the X's and Y's in the formal propositions of
mathematics by particular values depending on the particular science. This reduction, it seems to me, is less significant and ultimate
than has been supposed, because I think it can only be upheld by
one who follows to the uttermost the same methods of handling relations and systems which Frege applied to arithmetic. Frege, instead

of considering three apples and three trees as being each three by virtue of partaking in some Platonic *three* stored up somewhere in heaven, reversed the process and made the number three itself consist of the *class of all triads,* evading the apparent circle by defining some specific triad in terms of its identities and differences, and other triads in terms of one-one correspondence with the first. We should have to apply this same method to implication, the great form of systematic connection, and deny there was, alongside of and in addition to space, time, causal relations, and so on, a relation called *implication;* but saying rather that implication is a whole *class of relations,* otherwise of very diverse sorts, which all have certain precise formal properties. (We should be careful, I may remark in passing, to call these relations complex relations, or some such name, since they hold between complex terms which themselves contain relations, e.g., a R b. ⊃. c S d, so that complex relations are not dyadic, triadic, etc.) That is, there is no one relation called implication, subsisting by itself; there is simply a certain characteristic of certain complex relations which leads us to call a group of them the implication relations. My former naïve and childlike confidence that certain facts implied other facts has been even more rudely shaken by discovering that in Whitehead and Russell's *Principia Mathematica* implication turned out to be not only not a relation but not even a class of relations among facts, but that it was a class of relations between symbols, not between facts at all. "Either-or" is not a physical relation, it is a certain symbolic way of taking things, such as Husserl calls a "categoric" relation, and implication is defined as "either not p or q." Implication is in the *Principia* a certain combination of symbols, which is built up of component symbols, which combination has a certain parallelism with the structure of the members of a certain *class of complex relations among facts* (the *class of implication relations,* if I may so call them). The bearing of this on our conception of scientific law and of the supposed elimination of causality and the substitution for it of mathematical functionality expressed as implication, is very significant. Systematic connection among objective facts is not implication; what stands for implication objectively is a certain class of systematic relations, the implication relations, which may be causal, etc., in diverse ways. There is no physical relation which is one of being mere implication without being something more also, and I therefore believe that the supposed reduction of all systematic connection to mathematical connection is something of an illusion.

Now for our main thesis, which has to do with the work of estimating probabilities. In an essay published by A. A. Cournot in 1851, entitled *The Foundations of Our Knowledge*, he distinguished, and I think correctly, between what he calls mathematical probability and what he calls rational probability. We have mathematical probability where we are dealing with an atomic make-up of things, as for instance, when we are picking balls out of a bag, counting them, returning, and mixing, as in the popular examples in the books on probability, our purpose there being to estimate the proportion of black and white. I understand Venn to maintain this is the only sort of probability there is, and that there is *nothing in* the supposition that there exists another more a priori probability, the probability, for instance, that since a coin has two sides, it will fall half one way and half the other. Suppose, for the sake of argument, that Venn is right. Then I submit that it is an extraordinary coincidence that arguments which have no foundation whatever should so frequently come out correct, and that where there is a discrepancy, this itself should so frequently have been easily foreseeable by the same methods. It is an extraordinary coincidence that the coin actually should fall half and half, the tetrahedron once in four and the die once in six, and when for instance, the die fails so to fall, it should be possible to find, before throwing at all, that the center of gravity is not at the intersection of the diagonals. Furthermore, were Venn consistent, I maintain it would be invalid for him to argue, from the fact that a homogeneous wooden cube fell with a specified side uppermost approximately one in six, to any probability that a homogeneous ivory die would fall so also, because what they have in common is six-sidedness, and it is, by hypothesis, invalid to base an argument on six-sidedness.

Those who contend for a type of probability which has an a priori element seem to me to be right in so doing, but wrong in supposing the proposition "The die will fall a given side up once in six," is an a priori proof and not a hypothesis. Let me explain what I mean by hypothesis, as this is fundamental in the understanding of the sort of probability I have in mind. If I make a guess that a copper coin lying before me on the table will, if I toss it up, fall three times heads out of six, that is not a hypothesis, in spite of the fact that it may be confirmed or refuted by experience. Suppose I throw it, and it does come heads up three out of six. This verifies my guess, but it does not verify any hypothesis, because the amount of information about the coin I have at the end is exactly the same as if I had made no guess at all. It is wrong, therefore, to suppose every guess is a hypothesis. The verification of a true hypothesis by an experience must increase my information at a more rapid rate than do the mere observational data by which the verification comes about. This can be the case only when there exist in the objects observed certain systematic connections, which systematic connections the hypothesis declares to exist. When a hypothesis is about a system of heterogeneous elements A, B, C, D, the verification of D may make probable [the verification] of A, B, and C, which may each be very unlike D. For instance, by observing the swing of a pendulum, I may render more probable a formula for the rate of fall of a stone, or another formula for the orbit of the moon, and this is possible because it verifies the law of gravitation, itself a hypothesis about systematic connections. In short, when we verify a hypothesis we render probable not merely the existence of further similar phenomena but always also of phenomena different from, often very heterogeneous with, those we observe.[58] It ought, therefore, to be obvious that the sort of probability we get when we verify a hypothesis is radically different from mathematical probability as above defined. We may call it, with Cournot, rational probability, or better still systematic probability. Pulling balls out of a bag will

[58]   See Appendix A, below, pp. 191–92.

give a mathematical probability about other balls still in the bag, but it will tell you very little about anything heterogeneous, for instance what will be found if you pull eggs out of a nest. Not so when you verify a hypothesis, and the results you reach about the polarization of light may be rendering more probable a whole variety of phenomena, say phenomena of interference and the like.

Hypothesis involves a more intimate combination of the deductive with the inductive than is currently supposed. We are told there are three stages, hypothesis, deduction, and verification, as if the deduction were all in the second stage and the empirical observation made the totality of the third. I believe more enters into the deduction stage than purely formal reasoning, for reasons I have partly indicated in my discussion above about system in logic and system in fact, and I doubt if a mathematician could, unaided, make the suitable deductions from a hypothesis in chemistry or geology. And into verification there seems to me to enter a notion of systematic connection which raises verification above the simple empirical observing of the same phenomena. This latter brings about a higher probability than can come from mathematical probability estimated from the same observations. Given a die, I fully agree that, prior to all experience, even though you know it to be of homogeneous material, you cannot say six will fall uppermost one time out of six. But I do assert that you can generalize more widely and surely from a very little experience than you could if you were simply told the results 1 to 6, without knowing how they came about.

Another consideration is dwelt upon by Cournot and has since been also insisted upon by Charles Peirce. Given three points on a diagram, representing a certain phenomenon, say points at abscissae 0, 1, 2, you can draw an infinity of curves through these points. The point on the curve with abscissa 3 may have any value. But if we, without knowing what curve is correct, select a point with abscissa 3 determined by one certain simple equation among all the possible equations of curves passing through the three points, and if observation verifies our calculation, the probability that this equation represents the phenomena is obviously greatly increased. Yet no mathematical probability can be given for this, since there are also an infinity of possible curves which would pass through four points as well as through three. This will illustrate the complete failure of mathematical probability to deal with systematic connections.

I have indicated above in the first section the error of the notion that systematic connection belongs in some realm of mathematics which is unique and totally non-empirical or at least radically distinct from mere empirical connections. I have indicated that the mathematical connections are the empirical connections themselves, but whole classes of them taken as groups; that there is, for example, this causal connection and yonder spatial connection, and the whole group of them, provided each possesses a certain precise abstract property, is called implication—so far, indeed, as the latter is not further limited merely to the symbols for these. There are, then, systematic connections in the empirical world. It is more important to get a hold on these objective and concrete systematic connections than it is to estimate probabilities of any isolated atomic phenomena. You can get a better idea in a briefer time of the contents of a book on geometry if you trace the systematic connections of the first few proofs than if you select theorems at random throughout the book. Nature has her systems also, yet most statistical science goes at the questions as if the world were a grab-bag, a heap of disconnected phenomena, and the question were to take samples and generalize by mathematical probability: three red objects out of five, therefore thirty out of fifty. Luckily system creeps in in spite of efforts to keep it out, and systematic probability supersedes mathematical probability. I sum up by a thesis which I have many times repeated: The work of induction is not primarily to estimate mathematical probability, but by analysis and hypothesis to arrive at those key-relations which are central and fundamental in the various interwoven systems which constitute Nature.

April 28, 1914

ℰ NOTES

Stupendous!

[*Royce*]: Review of C. S. Peirce.[59] Logic [of] relatives, philosophy, correspondence, mathematics, statistics (Harvard Observatory and Coast Survey), reviews in *Nation*. Hard to place philosophically. Experience in mathematics and philosophy, scholastic logic. Hoped to write history of science. Variety of erudition and ingenuity. Not a coöperator. First edition of *Century Dictionary* (natural sciences). "Duns Scotus regarding principle of individuation"! Not faddish, no systematic delusions. Benjamin Peirce was fragmentary also, but officially more possible. [C. S. Peirce] anticipated philosophic applications of logic. Interested in "impractical side"! Russell: *Foundations of Geometry*, then Peano school, then concept of relation, and at about 1900 studied one of Peirce's two theories of relations.

Dr. Woods: Statistical controversy with Cattell; a statistical fallacy made by Woods. Can't separate heredity and environment but in a particular trait, and a particular difference in a particular environment can find environment ineffective. Monarchs: natural selection, not opportunity. Older and younger sons: younger might well be as good as older sons. Younger sons more numerous; 60% of all royalty are not monarchs, [Cattell pointed out]. [Woods] did have selected group, [but then] went over unselected group:

[59] Peirce had died on April 14, 1914. Victor F. Lenzen, as he has written to the editor, went to Milford, Pennsylvania, in December, 1914, and packed the Peirce papers for shipment to Harvard, where Royce then considered arrangements for their publication. Southard also, a short time before his death in 1920, worked on plans to edit them; see Gay, *The Open Mind*, p. 286.

after all, more than half of royalty *are* monarchs; total number of sons [averages] two-plus (four and a half in family)—54% monarchs. Now not a selected group. Couldn't appeal to opportunity. Historical method correct. No great tendency for high grades to be filled by monarchs (who have longer life slightly). ([To be] published in *Science*.) [60] Question was, does the particular environment, the royal office, lead to [intellectual] prominence? Answer: No, but [rather] the germ plasm counts. Formerly [Woods] had [included] maternal grandparents [in his statistical table], which could be found best for [a high ratio of] such older sons, etc. Other criticisms by Cattell. Older psychologists, especially sociologists, are environmentalists; germ-plasm workers on other side.

Royce: Cattell less synthetic than Thorndike, etc., but an extremely keen critic though sympathetic. Interested in editorial and administrative details. [His] criticism of Carnegie foundations.

Woods [sic]: Cattell's ideal the furtherance of science in America.

Royce: Lovejoy: Philosophy is correction of error—negative. Cattell individualistic but positive.

Woods: In Paris and London, *Science* and *Popular Science Monthly* not to be found.

Royce: Science less interesting than *Nature*. Cattell does not criticize English style.

Miss Webster: [Paper.] Concept of organic unity. Hobhouse's discussion of mechanism and teleology. (I) Various kinds of unity; (II) which are called organic unity; (III) biological conception of organism; (IV) Hobhouse's view.

[I] Oneness or simplicity. As Dewey points out, unity is equated with totality too often. (1) Many independent of the one, (2) parts dependent on whole, and whole less so, (3) all equally dependent. (1a) Given the parts, you know all, e.g. aggregate; no real connection, series (?), etc. (1b) Way they are put together: parts more prominent, systematized by some law external to parts, A different

[60] Woods, "Sovereigns and the Supposed Influence of Opportunity," *Science*, N.S. XXXIX (June 19, 1914), 902–05.

from B (Russell, *Principles of Mathematics*). Machine; corporation; "mechanical unity," or even "organic unity," organization
rather than organism. (2) Whole: absolute monism in philosophy;
chemical unity; organic unity; possibly, society. (3) Whole and
parts—Hegel: plant and animal life.

[II] "Organic unity" means (1) whole more than sum, (2) parts
determined by whole, [or](3) [whole and parts] equal. Apply to
society: (1) corporation, (2) [a] number [of] individuals, (3)
mutual. Character vs. actions: (1),(2),(3). Third type is what is
really meant. (Is there anything equally one and many?) Community ([Royce], *The Problem of Christianity*, Vol. II) is many
in deeds and one in language, customs, religion, and social consciousness; many in present, one in past and future.

[III] Biology reduces to mechanism, or contrasts with [it]
sharply. Mechanism may mean (1) model, (2) mathematical
equations, [or] (3) causal law (philosopher's), i.e., necessary succession of efficient causes. Organism may mean (1) other than material determinants, e.g., purposes, (2) statistical laws, no mechanism, [or] (3) [something] indeterminate, or else teleology (final
causes), explained by values. Valuable end, means, and relation
between. Teleology complicated by psychological references to
purpose, also determination by future. Mechanism and teleology
are (1) exclusive, (2) different standpoints, [or] (3) teleology
more adequate—Haldane; on a different, higher, plane.

[IV] Hobhouse: Mechanism as a machine, a continuous strand,
self-contained, continuous, active, independent; same cause same
effect; typical reaction to typical conditions. Machine (1) many
independent causal series, [which] (2) interweave and control
[in] (3) time required for this intereffect. (4) Needs a maker?
Organism in plant and animal. Internal principle and close adjust-
ment. Interactions become so rapid the time is zero and all work
together. Purpose [is] internal and not external. Any part acts
with the whole; thus differs in kind: [is] teleological. Teleology:
The Theory of Knowledge, 1896, held [that the conception of teleology is derived from] conscious human action and [involves] value,

etc. Intelligent mind; distinction of means and end and process. Organism quasi-teleological. In *Development and Purpose:* result and action condition one another, so teleology is organism. Action determined by future? Value drops out. (Not Russell's view that time is not objective.) Not clear as to future. [You] make [a] tool because it will do something; clear when there is *mind.* In case of organism—seems to need a mind. Mechanism and teleology [occupy the] same sphere. Induction to find which. In Russell's attack, Hobhouse's concept of cause is overthrown. But presence of psychical element still separates organic. But is this true? Haldane has two realms (*Mechanism, Life, and Personality*), the one more concrete; leaves out consciousness and emphasizes the *whole.*

Problems: (1) Whole and part equal? Reference to time? (Hobhouse: psychical.) (2) Organism and mechanism—are they on a level (Hobhouse) or at different levels (Haldane)? (Hobhouse: possible development of organic and inorganic.)

Brogan: Value the important question in teleology. Hobhouse confused as to what he means by value.

Royce: How define in terms of value?

Brogan: Teleology is the temporal arriving at value, increase of value, in a selected part of the world. Must be some relation between process and the value.

Royce: Organism?

Brogan: No. But . . . world without organisms would be without value. But [there] might *be* organisms, without value.

Woods: Why restrict value to organisms?

Brogan: Seems to me organism only has value.

Troland: Teleology in terms of value needs statistical work.

Brogan: One case sufficient.

Troland: Either conscious purpose or else general law.

Royce [to] Brogan: Greek teleology not conscious. Siebeck, *Geschichte der Psychologie.* Davidson held Aristotle knew nothing of consciousness. In later times, discussion of memory, etc. (If there is any one modern concept of consciousness.) Hypothesis that non-consciousnesses are "rundown consciousnesses"—Cope

Hyatt, Peirce, etc. Lamarckians. What we do with care is later habit. In social cases, inventions of a social order are not performed by any one person; insurance, banking, etc. Their teleology is not in proportion to their consciousness. Grammar of a language, e.g., early Greek; Greek literature preceded rhetoric and grammar. English common law.

Troland: Fechner maintained atomization of action and hence social oversoul.

Royce: The social consciousness is not aware what literature is good for when it invents. Language a work of social genius neither God nor man could foresee.

Brogan: All part of one process, therefore not accidental.

Royce: Goethe and Bergson.

Woods: Chance?

Royce: Is beyond expectations of chance? Then fecundity of aggregation—Peirce. Discussions of aggregates fail to recognize that, in the wholly mathematical world, philosophers have not recognized how many structures there are analogous to organic: mere aggregation or that plus something more. Linear triad and nonlinear triad, and "between": is such a mere aggregate? Unity? Yes—not organic. All descriptive geometry arises from *between.* What is "sum of its parts"? Simplest organic relation, ϵ.[61] Man and community. Study mathematical logic.

[Next]: Eliot, subject-matter of psychology.

April 28, 1914

&~ SUMMARY

At the beginning of the meeting Professor Royce mentioned the death of C. S. Peirce, and traced briefly some of Peirce's accom-

---

61 Cf. *Principia Mathematica,* I, 25.

plishments and his unfinished plans. He characterized Peirce as a man of great erudition and originality, whose work was handicapped by his being temperamentally unable to coöperate with others, and by his lack of clarity in the exposition of his views.

Dr. F. A. Woods then summarized a discussion he had had with Professor Cattell, concerning a statistical fallacy in the book by Woods entitled *The Influence of Monarchs*. The question was whether a certain environment, namely that of the royal office, conduced to prominence, or whether heredity determined, rather than environment, who should rise to fame. Dr. Woods said there were as many famous younger sons as elder sons, though only the latter inherited the throne. Professor Cattell replied that Dr. Woods drew his statistics from a selected group and that there were more younger sons than elder, hence naturally more chance that some should be famous. The criticism was correct as regards the original statistics; but by revised statistics Dr. Woods was able to show that the influence of the mere possession of the royal office was devoid of noteworthy effect. Hence in this particular case heredity meant more than environment.

Professor Royce characterized Cattell as a keen critic though a less synthetic mind than Thorndike; and [?Dr. Woods] said Cattell's great ideal was the furtherance of science in America.

Miss Webster then read a paper on "The Concept of Organic Unity." She first considered various kinds of unities: (1) those in which the parts are more prominent, including (a) aggregates and (b) mechanisms; (2) those in which the whole is more prominent, such as chemical unities (there being some people who hold societies to be of this type, and others, the monistic philosophers, who consider all the universe to be such a whole superior to its parts); and (3) those unities in which whole and part are equal or nearly so.

Secondly, Miss Webster remarked that organic unity had been identified with each of the above unities, except possibly the mere aggregate. She held the best definition was that which made whole and part equally important—for instance the definition of the community which says it is many in the present but one in memory and ideal.

Thirdly, she considered the biological concept of organism, which may be either mechanistic or teleological. Mechanism may mean (1) similar to some material model, or (2) predictable by mathematical equations, or (3) determined by a necessary succession of efficient causes. Those who believe organisms do not reduce to pure mechanisms hold (1) there are present some such non-material determinants as purposes; or (2) physical laws are statistical and not mathematically exact; or else (3) there is some sort of attainment of value which is more than mechanism, though possibly not involving conscious purpose. Of the two, mechanism and teleology, it may be held that they are (1) mutually exclusive or (2) two sides of the same thing, or (3) that teleology is a more adequate and higher account, including and transcending mechanisms.

Miss Webster devoted the remainder of her paper to a consideration of Hobhouse's attempt to reconcile mechanism and teleology. Hobhouse's theory is that in the purely physical world, when objects interact, the interactions take a certain time, but in the organism, although the interactions between the organism and its environment take place slowly, those between the parts of the organism itself are practically instantaneous. The result is that the whole organism acts as a unit, hence according to its total nature which is more or less unique. Miss Webster thought Hobhouse had not sufficiently explained why this sort of behavior should be teleological, and said he seemed to settle the question by introducing consciousness into all biological phenomena.

In the discussion, Mr. Brogan claimed that attainment of value, not purpose, was the fundamental characteristic of teleology. He was disposed to hold all extrinsic value relative to the existence of organisms (organizations) and the existence of organisms to be the only thing possessed of intrinsic worth.

In answer to Mr. Brogan's query what evidence there was that consciousness was present from the beginning of organic life, Professor Royce pointed to the fact that in our own life what later becomes a habit had first to be consciously acquired, and the same might be generalized to include even the lowest organic reflexes. But in the case of societies there seems to be a teleology which is with difficulty explained as any sort of conscious foreseeing. The people who create a language do not foresee the great literature which may be written in that language. Mr. Troland claimed this was evidence for Fechner's social over-soul, but Professor Royce declared it seemed there were some results accomplished by a society such that apparently neither God nor man could foresee.

Professor Royce then added that in the discussion of organic unities too little attention had been paid to the mathematical world. Is a relation of "betweenness" a mere aggregate; or again does not the *epsilon* relation, that between a member and a class, have in it something more than mere togetherness?

May 5, 1914

ໄ NOTES

[*?Royce*]: "Immortality of man for the current year" runs an opposition show.[62]

Royce to Brogan: What of definition of fitness, as given at beginning of course? Case of Algol variables.

Brogan: Extrinsic values.

Royce: Take a synthesis wide enough and you get an intrinsic good. No conscious purpose needed.

Brogan: Teleology is attainment of good by a process, not by pure accident.

[62] On the evening of May 5, in Emerson D, the lecture hall adjoining the seminar room, G. F. Foote, Frothingham Professor of the History of Religion, delivered the annual Ingersoll Lecture on the Immortality of Man, his subject being "Metempsychosis."

Royce: Henderson uses teleology as not a purposive process. Vitalism vain.

Eliot: [Paper.] [63] Classification of *Gegenstände höherer Ordnung,* different types of objects. Not metaphysical categories—empirical. A theory of their relations metaphysical. Not Kantian categories. Meinong considers objects *per se.* An analysis of objects into complexes of sense-data does not give anything necessarily more real. Things—real things, including unreal (*useless*)—are normal objects. Do not begin with sense-data. Atoms the ultimate, perhaps. Bundle of sense-data will be only sense-data; a thing is made of other *things.* Universals and relations are a third type. [A] thing is [the] standard object. Classes another type; space and time another; perhaps causality. Certainly mental [objects]—ideas, feelings, emotions, will, signs, conscious persons; and social objects—institutions. Round [and] square, imagination, etc., perhaps are *founded* objects, not unreal as objects but as things. Hallucination is founded, and not a thing. Ideas like relations are not things; cf. first chapter of Bradley's *Logic.* We tend to treat objects as things. If there were no things, these would be things. An idea is, e.g., the fulfillment of purpose; but this is another idea. A sign qua sign is not an object in the same sense as the object. In [an] idea there is only the *reference* and not the material part of the sign. Then there are facts. Then perhaps God!

Important question is alteration of type [of object] as in sense-data. Cf. Stout, [*A Manual of Psychology*]: perception of [a] triangle [is] not triangular. [But it is] wrong to say it is not triangular. Nonsense. Idea wrongly thought to have existence apart from reference. An idea is an abstraction from itself. [There] appear confusions in ethics: do we desire pleasure or a thing or a fact?—each true in its own way. We frequently treat one type [of object] as

---

63 The origins of this paper might shed light on Eliot's idea of the "objective correlative" (*Selected Essays 1917–1932,* pp. 124–25); cf. James Ward's concept of the Ego and the correlative non-Ego (*Psychological Principles,* Cambridge, 1918). The phrase itself has been traced by R. W. Stallman to Washington Allston.

another, e.g., in social sciences. Psychology has no objects (ideas, soul, etc., are objects but are not freeable from their *inferiora*). Parallelism [of] psychological [and] physical involves a confusion of types. In what sense is an idea a sign? Somewhat related. Sign may be misinterpreted or not recognized, not an idea. Part of content cut off. Fox sign of cunning. Heterogeneous with event. But how can idea be a sign? Its apartness from what it means is very evanescent.[64]

Subject-matter of psychology. Prichard: two types of psychology, mental content and psychological process. Content is in one context, object in another—Wodehouse, Witasek, Höfler. When you consider a sensation of red as cognitive, you know the object; later you turn to "red," a uniquely determined one. Object is presented to consciousness but [is] not a presentation. A red object, otherwise known than by the quality red, is in an order. We sense a red spot. Stout says an object belongs to psychology as known to an individual mind. But then can we study it as related to a mind? Cigar known to smoker, known to psychology, and known to psychology as known to smoker. Alexander: [in] conational psychology, including affection, [the] sensum [is] non-mental. Do away with presentation. Difficulty, again, in constructing a thing out of sensations: object and quality not distinct yet not same. Best theory that of Lipps, *Inhalt und Gegenstand:* Things given. We are conscious of thing. Self and its objects form one whole. Get psychological objects by turning in direction of Self (*Ich*). Mental states are relations which in one reference are external. Properties not things but experience with respect to a point of attention. (Cf. Ward: All from a certain point of view.) *Ich, Empfinden, Empfundene.* Color is a relation between myself and object but not separate, and makes up both. Can't be separated from both. Natural science is to get terms and relations belonging to a system. Appearance in relation to self would demand a whole universe of sciences. Lipps has mind essentially related to world. Abstract self and world along with it. Descriptive psychology deals with objects

64 A marginal note reads: "Hoernlé: image, idea, meaning."

which are probably not independent of *inferiora* (things) to which they refer. The idea is a constructed interpretation of behavior, no person with *one* idea. Behavior of other people and our own calls for ideas to interpret it. Idea can't be handled as a thing: disappears in two ways—physiological concomitants and things. No consciousness as an object: no such thing; consciousness is amateur metaphysics. Any philosophy which tries to interpret one type of object in terms of others is metaphysics and not description. In description one type of object is just as real and self-dependent as another.

Royce: Are types categories? Epistemological? Various objects are things or objects founded on things.

Eliot: Higher types not mental.

Royce: Distinguish by type of knowledge we have of them. Later: what type of object does psychology consider? Sensation a relational object.

Eliot: Question whether it can be handled independently of what it is a sensation of.

Royce: Theory of objects not treated in textbooks.

Eliot: Ideas I have considered most. Social objects have a greater independence.

Royce: Catholicism is not a mere abstraction; Buddhism; American or English Constitution. What types are here?

Eliot: Need to consider causality here? None of these objects are abstractions.

Van Riper: Higher?

Eliot: More founded on *things.*

Brogan: Are things physical? How is an emotion, for consciousness, founded on physical things?

Royce: Cf. James-Lange theory. Behaviorism.

Eliot: Amended behaviorism. In James' theory you have an illusion to explain. For me the emotion is real but there is a point of view from which it is reducible. Psychology reduces to physiology.

Brogan: This theory is metaphysical and not phenomenological.

Van Riper: Existence of emotion equals knowledge of it? "Ought" is judgment plus emotion, but most people think it is *why* the former.

Eliot: Emotion must be known.

Brogan: Behaviorism absurd as regards emotion. Fails to take account of facts. Needs to be cautiously presented.

Royce: Theory inarticulate yet. Doing vs. having consciousness of doing. Hypocrisy or lying about one's state of mind: e.g., "I've had a good time." Cases of hysteria and melancholia: we can see through our moods, but [the] hysterical cannot foresee mood will pass.

Eliot: In my theory there is something outside—e.g., beauty is outside, and distressed world, etc.

Royce: "They really think they are tempted, but they really aren't tempted."

May 5, 1914

৫ SUMMARY

The meeting began by a discussion between Professor Royce and Mr. Brogan concerning the definition of "fitness" given by Professor Royce at the beginning of the year. It was agreed that it was possible to speak of a value's being attained without calling in the satisfaction of a conscious purpose.

Mr. Eliot then read a paper treating first of the empirical classification of different types of objects, and secondly, in more detail, of the nature of those objects, if any, which furnish the peculiar subject-matter of psychology. The opinions stated were tentative in tone, and the range of topics so wide that any adequate summary is difficult. As regards the classification of objects, the paper was along the line of Meinong's proposed *Gegenstandstheorie*. It was not to be considered an attempt to make a list of metaphysical categories; it wished to find empirically what sorts of objects there were, and to suggest the fallacies which might arise in attempting to reduce these sorts to one another. The most immediately given objects are things, not sense-data, and it is impossible to reduce these to one another; the parts of things are not sense-data but other things. Other types of objects are possibly universals and relations, classes, space and time, causality, mental objects, social objects. Much of the discussion turned on the distinction between ideas and things. A sign is a thing plus a meaning; an idea is only a meaning. This led to the discussion of the subject-matter of psychology. Various theories were criticized; most favorably that of Lipps, to the effect that sensation is an intermediary between subject and object and inseparable from both, and this intermediary is the subject-matter of psychology. But no fully satisfactory theory has yet been advanced.

Professor Royce said he thought the richest territory for the study of different types of objects was the social realm. What sort of an object is Catholicism or the English Constitution? These are not to be called merely abstractions.

The discussion then turned to the behavioristic psychology and its adequacy. Mr. Brogan said it failed to take account of obvious facts. Professor Royce was less severe, but still urged that no sufficient behaviorist interpretation was as yet forthcoming of certain mental states, for example the state of the hypocrite or of certain hysterical patients who talk of suicide but act quite otherwise. Behaviorism may be able to account for these, but has not as yet done it.

May 12, 1914

ै NOTES

[*Royce*]: Logic in preliminary examinations. Implication: "Could God sin if he would?" Work of Lewis.[65] Power to abstract from whether you believe a doctrine.

[*Costello*]: Note on mathematical systems and on systematic probability.

Royce: Star drifts studied by mathematical probability. Case of Pearson vs. Mendelians, latter holding hypothesis of presence or absence. Pearson held to statistics of greater and less.

Troland: Common part in all. Functional part [is] something which affects our reasoning.

Royce: Non-Euclidean geometry, and parallel-column arrangement possible [between it and Euclidean geometry]. Or point equals circle, and line [equals] system of circles.

Costello: This is partly generalization.

Troland: Point of formal similarity.

Costello: Laws deducible because they have a common part.

Royce: Only in case of elimination.

Troland: Electron and atom.

Chemical origin of regulation of life, enzymes, next time.

---

[65] C. I. Lewis, "Implication and the Algebra of Logic," *Mind,* N.S. XXI (October, 1912), 522–31; "Interesting Theorems in Symbolic Logic," *Journal of Philosophy,* X (April 24, 1913), 239–42; "A New Algebra of Implications and Some Consequences," *Journal of Philosophy,* X (July 31, 1913), 428–38; "The Calculus of Strict Implication," *Mind,* N.S. XXIII (April, 1914), 240–47. Lewis and Costello had been fellow students in the seminar of 1909–10. Both Costello and Royce were of course familiar with Lewis' theory of strict implication apart from his published papers on the subject.

May 12, 1914

&ᴥ SUMMARY

Most of the meeting was taken up by the comments Professor Royce made on the preliminary doctorate examinations in logic, the present general low level of logical study and teaching at Harvard, and the hope that the coming year would see a pronounced improvement in these regards.[66] Particularly were students who took the examination ignorant of the nature of implication, of the fact that a false proposition implies all propositions. Hence they had not seen that, to the question discussed by St. Thomas Aquinas, "Could God sin if he would?" the answer was in the affirmative. (Comment: I examined Mr. Russell on these questions. He "flunked" completely on the St. Thomas one!) Professor Royce then called attention to Dr. Lewis' discussion of the question whether a false proposition implies all propositions. Professor Royce held Dr. Lewis had wrongly introduced questions of our knowledge and psychological powers, since he had wished to define *implies* as "can be deduced from." These formal questions are worth discussing, for a student should acquire the power to study the implications of a doctrine—abstraction made from whether or no he believes it.

Dr. Costello then read a note on two topics: one on the nature of the so-called logical entities, insisting on their abstractness; the other on the contrast between statistical probability and the kind of probability you get when you verify a hypothesis, which may be called systematic probability. When entities are tied together by systematic laws, these enter not merely into the deduction of

[66] An instance of Costello's "puckishness": any improvement in the teaching of logic at Harvard would follow his own departure for Yale.

the consequences of hypotheses about them, but also into the value of a given verification, and enable us often to reach a higher degree of probability than mere generalization from statistical averages would enable us to reach.

Professor Royce brought up various cases, which were discussed in this regard: Kapteyn's star drifts, Mendelism, the curious parallelism between Euclidean and non-Euclidean geometry, etc.

Mr. Troland held that systematic probability was not, as Dr. Costello had called it, "probability of the heterogeneous," many diverse entities being rendered probable by belonging to the same system with entities whose existence was verified; but that their probability was due to an element of identity running through the entire system and partaken in by each. Thus systematic probability was statistical probability applied to his abstract element of identity. Dr. Costello thought it doubtful that a deductive system was rendered what it was by a thread of identity running through it.

Comment: One of the great difficulties in logic teaching is the use of terms in different ways. An example is the term "inference." Professor Royce said, at the last meeting: "What must be the state of mind of a candidate for the doctorate who says on his examination paper that from a false proposition nothing can be inferred! All ought to know," he added, "that one can draw true as well as false conclusions from one or more false premises: for instance, if all oysters are mortal and Socrates is an oyster, then Socrates is mortal." Now, I have read too many examination papers in logic to doubt that it was statistically probable the state of mind of said student was very bad; but in so far as what was said was: "From a false proposition nothing can be inferred," this is quite in accordance with at least one possible precise definition of inference. It is doubtful, I admit, and a matter somewhat of convention, whether or no one calls the passage from the falsity of a proposition to the truth of its contradictory an inference. But I gather that what Professor Royce had in mind was something more, something based on other principles than the law of excluded middle, and to this his illustration bears witness. From

Socrates the oyster you infer Socrates mortal. Now you will find inference formulated in Whitehead and Russell's *Principia Mathematica,* *9·12, in the primitive proposition: "What is implied by a true premiss is true." From it we see that while a false premise implies everything, from it we can infer nothing, the doubtful case of the contradictory excepted. Unless "Socrates is an oyster" is a true premise, there is no logical inference from it. This is further explained under *1·1 that the principle of inference must be carefully distinguished from the hypothetical proposition: "If p is true, and if, if p then q, then q," which is true always, whether p is true or not and whether p implies q or not. What we wish to do in an inference is to be able to assert q simply. As is stated on p. 9 of the Introduction, "An inference is the dropping of a true premiss; it is the dissolution of an implication." If we keep this in mind, we shall not be disturbed much by the fact that a false proposition implies all propositions, for we shall remember that an implication is not an inference.

What Professor Royce had in mind as constituting inference (and what Mr. Brogan had in mind, I think, in a definition of necessary implication he proposed to me during the week), was the building up, or the observing, of implications which do not involve formal fallacies. That is, it is taken to be the observing of a certain sort of implication, whereas in the *Principia* it is an elimination of premises. A formal fallacy is any deductive form which would in at least one assignable case lead to false conclusions from true premises. For instance, if we say: "If all Englishmen are Europeans, and if all Londoners are Europeans, then all Londoners are Englishmen," we have a statement containing in it three true propositions, but we have nevertheless a formal fallacy, as would be evident if we substituted Parisians for Londoners. A formal fallacy always involves an appeal to generalization, a query whether it could ever lead from true antecedents to false consequents. When we speak of inference in Professor Royce's sense, we should distinguish it sharply from the sense in which the *Principia* uses inference. I should prefer to speak of the former as "formal implication" but the *Principia* uses this term to cover also cases like: "For all values of X, if X is a man, X is mortal," which might be false, for maybe some men are immortal. If I used Mr. Brogan's term "necessary implication," I should mean by it simply "formal general implication"; that is, replacing constants by apparent variables, the implication still holds. (If we replace man by Y and mortal by Z, the above formal implication will not hold.) But the point to be clear about is this, that in "If all oysters are mortal and if Socrates is an oyster, then Socrates is mortal," we do not have three propositions. We have one long proposition; and this proposition can be broken up, so as to give simply and without condition "Socrates is mortal," only if the two other parts are true propositions.

May I add a word about the definition of implication. I think Professor Royce is unfair to Dr. Lewis in interpreting his "can be inferred from" as having reference to our knowledge or our psychology. I am sure he means something other than that, but I also am not sure his criticism is really cogent. The ~ p v q interpretation of implication which makes a false proposition imply any proposition does no harm, since we can't infer from it (knowing ~ p v q and ~ p). But it does furnish a simple device for making our universe of discourse explicit. Suppose we are talking about cardinal numbers. We write: "Whatever X may be, if X is a cardinal number, then, etc." This proposition will then hold not merely for X's that are cardinal numbers but for all possible X's, the X's that are not cardinal numbers making the antecedent (or hypothesis) false, and thus the rest of the proposition indifferent, for the proposition as a whole is automatically satisfied; but the proposition will become worth while as soon as X is a cardinal number. So that a false proposition implies all propositions is harmless and very convenient. The real difficulty arises when we consider whether in the current usage of language we are disposed to say any two true propositions mutually imply and thus can be inferred from one another. Would the scientist be apt to infer: "Water is composed of hydrogen and oxygen," from "The sun is hot?" This I understand to be Dr. Lewis' point, and I think it a decidedly questionable metaphysical thesis to say if we knew enough we could infer one of these from the other. The real answer to Lewis I take to be this, that it is true we are able to infer empirically only where there is causal connection, but that causal connection is not a thing for logic to consider. The interpretation p v q is as far as logic can go, and from it no harm will ever be done, because we can never use it empirically unless we do know some general causal law or else observe that q, as a matter of fact, is true. Dr. Lewis does not introduce the subjective, but he does introduce something out of the scope of logic.

May 19, 1914

ଛ NOTES

Royce: Russell says philosophy reduces to logic—accessible and absolutely true; rest is physics, correlations. Induction—no account of latter.

[*?Costello*]: Reply: I admit mine has no foundation. Bergson has none but won't admit it.

Royce complimented Russell. Said he [Royce] felt like Arnold's "forsaken merman." Russell clear and ready to admit incompleteness. Englishmen find us too strident. [They] may be radical, but [are] not assertive. Contrast with Roosevelt. Royce's meeting with Frazer of *The Golden Bough*, and latter's modesty. Same case with an officer in Indian Service. Scotchman also has it, e.g., James Seth. Voluble converser, etc., is Jacks of Manchester College, Oxford, but avoids "himself." In German scholars, we have self-assertion often, e.g., Harnack. Wundt interested more in *"die Sache selbst,"* Lotze constitutionally timid.

Royce: On topical examinations for doctorate.

Troland: On enzymes.[67] Example of hypothesis, and illustration of vitalism vs. mechanism. Enzyme as an explanatory agency; [it] unifies a number of laws: (1) origin-of-living-matter problem, (2) origin of organic variations, (3) ground of heredity, (4) mechanism of individual development, (5) basis of physiological regulation in mature organism. Difficulties for mechanism in these. Vitalists emphasize regulation and call it purposiveness. Enzyme provides us [with] a chemical principle of regulation. Can we apply it to all problems?

Source of all energy is chemical. "Catalyzers" is general head, including yeasts and [a] few other ferments. An enzyme is an organic catalyst (i.e., made up of carbon, hydrogen, oxygen, nitrogen, etc.). [A catalyst] hastens chemical reaction by mere presence, e.g., hydrogen, oxygen, and a piece of platinum block. A given enzyme generally furthers only a given chemical change.

Royce: "Negative enzymes"?

[*Troland*]: Answer: [they] "poise" other enzymes.

Royce: Friction?

[*Troland*]: Don't know.

Apply to the five problems:

(1) [Life] originated in sea. Suppose "accidentally" there is formed a certain enzyme, producing a simple oily substance not soluble. Grows, splits. But must suppose each new globule has some of enzyme, hence enzyme itself must grow. Autocatalysis, well known. Eoplasm not something which occurs at a stroke, for "simple protoplasm" is very complex; large number of different enzymes. Irritability and contractility.

(2) Origin of variations. Changes in question occur in single molecules or in few. Thus apparent chance-character of variations. Mutations rather than quantitative, because chemical substances

---

[67] A summary of Troland's "The Chemical Origin and Regulation of Life," *Monist,* XXIV (January, 1914), 92–133, where he had touched also (pp. 94–95) on the question of teleology in natural selection, considered in his note of January 20.

form a discrete series; De Vries and Mendel. Autocatalysis and "trap"; accidental production of a single molecule sufficient.

(3) Heredity in nucleus—Weismann. Difficulties [with his theory]: (a) Nucleus too small. (b) No mechanism suggested. Enzyme theory meets these [objections]. (c) Hereditary mechanism must be self-reproducing. Enzymes autocatalytic.

(4) [i.e., (5)] Enzyme gives us a clue how germ cell can control an entire organism. Certain in liver tissue, etc. Enzymes may determine planes of cleavage of cells and selective distribution of enzymes themselves. Makes Weismann's theory more specific.

Methodological: way in which theory binds together various facts. Mere presence determines; no energy used. Carbon is lethargic yet life is quick, due to enzymes. Self-reproductivity demanded by biology and provided. Small quantity furthers massive reactions. Variations provided for. Discrete character of chemical substances and *ditto* of mutations. A particular enzyme encourages only a particular reaction. Nucleus would reproduce itself. Enzymes are known to be very important in physiological processes.

Discussion.

Sen Gupta asked difference between organic and inorganic.

Van Riper: How can inside reproduce?

Costello: Accounts of what are catalysts?

[*?Troland*]: Electrical theory probably best.

Brogan: Where is empirical verification possible?

[*Troland*]: Answer: Some cases given. Synthesis possible?

Royce: Has anybody made any quasi-protoplasm?

[*Troland*]: Answer: Simple protoplasm is not simple.

Royce: Do you get even any "oil drops"? Cf. Tyndall's Belfast Address—referred to Plateau's experiment. Clerk Maxwell made fun of it. One ought to get reproduction at least by enzyme processes. Ostwald used to insist on catalysis, in *Naturphilosophie*. Challenge experimental verification of some sort.

[*?Troland*]: Another side: not proof, but what a theory can do is to unify and describe.

[*Royce*]: Yes, but can you deduce new results to be expected?

Royce said: Complex compounds have been held to be enough, but no one has done it. Just so with enzymes. All life has enzymes, yes; but what then? You propose a retroduction only.

Troland: Ought to be possible to find organic enzymes outside of protoplasm, e.g., submicroscopic bacteria—e.g., measles and smallpox.

Royce: Ought to be enzyme processes not organic; there ought to be many intermediates. Minot dwells on faintness of hope of finding origin of life; Arrhenius on light-pressure transmission of living particles. Dr. Raymond Pearl on "Present Methods in Genetics and Their Limitations." [68] Trained in statistical methods: Pearsonian and especially Mendelian. Head of experimental-agriculture station in Maine. Studying eggs and egg-laying. Danger from finding an explanation rich enough to cover an already given mass of facts. "Curve fitting": you can get far more laws than you would suppose; two curves may equally well fit your facts.

&v SUMMARY

May 19, 1914

Professor Royce took occasion at the beginning of the hour to say a few words about Mr. Russell's visit to Harvard, and the latter's modesty as to his own views and achievements. Professor Royce gave examples of the same type of character in other Englishmen, and contrasted it with the strident self-assertiveness of any German or American who has done something.

Mr. Troland then read a paper on enzymes as the explanation of life phenomena, showing how it was possible in terms of cata-

[68] Pearl read his paper in Boston on May 17, 1914, and Royce presumably heard it then. It was published as the opening chapter of Pearl's *Modes of Research in Genetics* (New York, 1915).

lytic actions which hastened chemical changes to explain mechanically: (1) the origin of living matter, (2) the origin of organic variations, (3) the ground of heredity, (4) the mechanism of individual development, and (5) the basis of physiological regulation in a mature organism. Carbon is ordinarily lethargic, and it needs some such theory as the enzymes afford to explain the quickness of changes in living matter. Mr. Troland claimed for his hypothesis its power to unify a great variety of facts, and the evidence from the known physiological importance of certain enzymes.

The discussion which followed turned chiefly on the sort of empirical verification possible, Professor Royce challenging Mr. Troland to produce novel deductions from his theory of such a sort as could be put to an empirical test.

In closing the discussion Professor Royce referred to a recent paper by Dr. Raymond Pearl on "Present Methods in Genetics and Their Limitations," wherein it was pointed out how easy it was to formulate an empirical law fitting a group of known facts, for instance a given diagrammatic curve. You can get far more such laws, all equally near to the facts, than you would at first suppose possible; hence the explanatory power of any one of them is rather small.

End for 1913–14.

ॐ APPENDIX A

Recollections of Royce's Seminar on Comparative Methodology [69]

HARRY TODD COSTELLO

Nearly forty years ago I saw Josiah Royce at Harvard for the last time, the late spring of 1916. He asked me what I had been doing at Yale and Columbia, and as I left he followed me to the door and said, "Coe-stay-low, get out of Columbia, they'll never understand you down there." He was right, but a philosopher must expect to be misunderstood. It gets really bad when they understand you too well.

I worked closely with Royce for the last time in 1913–1914, when I acted as a recording secretary in his remarkable Seminar on Comparative Methodology. I took down as much as I could of each session without using shorthand, and began the next session with a summary and criticism, to tie the discussions together. It was said of Royce in this Seminar that he put out a challenge to anybody who had some idea to come in and fight. By 1913, under doctor's warning, he dared not let loose the pugnacity which they say made him a terror in the '90s, a flaming red-haired apparition. The hair had turned yellow, and the thin lips quivered in a whim-

[69] An address read at a meeting of the Conference on Methods in Philosophy and the Sciences, at the New School for Social Research, November 20, 1955, the centenary of Royce's birth. Published in the *Journal of Philosophy*, LIII (February 2, 1956) 72–77. The editor has here made minor corrections.

sical smile, but he could still bite at times. He said there was one subject he did not know enough about to discuss, and that was economics. When Socrates said he did not know, that was the time to look out. When I quoted a passage from Veblen about modern science substituting continuous process for step by step cause and effect, under the influence of contemporary assembly-line technology, Royce straightened up to protest, "The man knows nothing about the history of thought. His novel idea was old stuff when Heraclitus was a boy." Royce tried to get visitors to come in and do their stuff. I remember Thomas Nixon Carver, classical economist, Irving Babbitt, enemy of Rousseau, Minot from the medical school. But also there were distinguished visitors who came again and again. In 1913–1914 there were particularly Lawrence Henderson, biological chemist; E. E. Southard, first head of the new Psychopathic Hospital in Boston; and Frederick Adams Woods of Mass. Tech, applying statistical methods to the heredity of the royal families of Europe. Both Woods and Royce kept reporting from time to time letters from Charles Peirce in Pennsylvania, until one spring day they had to comment sadly on the death of Peirce. In the spring Bertrand Russell arrived at Harvard after delay—I gave the preparatory lectures in his logic course. Russell never visited the Seminar, but Royce commented from time to time, for instance on the hard beauty of his style in the first Lowell Lecture on *Scientific Method in Philosophy*. Schröder's term, *harte Schönheit*, he said; for Schröder, symbolic logician, "loved cool precision, but there never was any thinker sloppier than Schröder himself." Of the students that year there were Headley, Ralph Blake, Van Riper, Hefelbower, Sen Gupta, and Miss Webster, in addition to three I shall speak of later, making nine. Hoernlé and Loewenberg dropped in occasionally, when teaching duties permitted.

The year's discussion started with Henderson's book, *The Fitness of the Environment*. Henderson had reported that the earth is fitted for life because of numerous peculiarities of the most abundant chemicals. He was afraid someone might take this, not as a report of facts, but a surrender to vitalism and the purposes of God. I remember his Charles Evans Hughes beard, and his squeaky voice rising shrill. Royce came in, the first day of papers, with a little paper of his own, on the definition of the concept of "fitness." The definition ran, "A fitness is some exceptional case or coincidence which fulfills an objective value." This launched us into days of argument, thrown into the midst of later discussions.

After Henderson, E. E. Southard came along next with a study he had been making of delusions. He said delusions he found to be connected not with the sensory but with the motor side of the mind; indeed all thinking is motor, not sensory. Southard attracted me; it was rumored he was a genius and a master as an amateur chess player, "a five or six game man blindfold." He told of playing cubical chess with a friend. In these present degenerate days *Time* carries pictures of a chess cube made of layers of glass plates. But Southard and his friend just carried the whole thing "in their heads," and fought it out in the middle of a non-existent cube. We raised the question of extraordinary space-imagery. He replied he never had any imagery at all, he just knew where everything was. Occasionally he might see a hand come out and grasp a pawn and vanish. There was language to communicate, but the language was not the game. Thinking would be confused by images. Royce remarked in confirmation that he had "felt Hamlet before him in delightful vividness, but when he tried to introspect found nothing but scraps of imagery." Southard said concepts are more exact than images, consciousness is like an electric sign that flashes off and on, but thinking is motor on its own right, not unconscious brain relays.

There was another genius in the group, this time a student, his name Troland, who later helped give "Technicolor" to the world. He summarized for us new ideas about the special theory of relativity and about statistical laws of nature and quanta. Royce was very much interested in sampling and probability, and the hard work needed to get random samples. I maintained that sampling the deductions from a hypothesis might increase the probability of things rather remote from the characters of the samples; and that Bragg space lattices in a crystal were two at first disconnected and doubtful hypotheses leading to a common highly exact verification by observations; also that the verification of a detective's hypothesis about a single event was different from an Einstein worldwide hypothesis—or was it? Troland held that when qualitatively different things are made probable by the same bits of evidence, there must be a hidden identity running through them. I said essential relation or system, not identity. There was much discussion of hypotheses throughout the year. Another question was whether there was room for spontaneity, for instance of mind, in a world of law. Royce and I argued there was no one world formula in sight, and any set of laws could be supplemented, as being necessary but not sufficient, as in physics, which accepts the laws of mathematics and goes beyond. Troland seemed still to feel the conservation of energy law ruled out mind, except as the inner side of matter, for he was a panpsychist. I thought this was orthodox conservatism with a lunatic fringe.

Albert P. Brogan, later at the University of Texas, was another student who was an alert critic throughout the year. On March 24, 1914, he finally brought forward a theory that the fundamental value concept was "the better" and not "the good." He had been trying to work out formal postulates for a value theory, and found "the better" had formal advantages. In terms of the better one could define both the good and the bad. Without discussing here the later development by Brogan and Mitchell, I would like to indicate some non-formal additional considerations. There is a contrast between the values of appreciation and the values of preference. Starting with the former, one might emphasize the aspect of pleasure or interest or satisfaction as a factor in all conscious awareness. Possibly these terms have their ambiguities. Conscious awareness, being connected with physical reactions, might cause a self-examining amoeba to state his ethical creed, "If it feels good, I stand pat; if it feels bad, I wiggle." Such blind reactions may lead by trial and error to the conserving of successful wiggles in acquired habits. From such small beginnings the hedonist and emotional ethics have grown. But satisfactions or interests or pleasures furnish no adequate serializing relations, except one of mere quantity. Pushpin turns out to be as good as poetry—or should we now say pinball and poetry? Let us turn to the opposing ethics of preference, which is intellectual, and therefore, if Southard was right, motor rather than sensory. It is not as crudely physically motor as was Hobbes. Hobbes defined religion as little motions away from power invisible—what direction is away from the invisible I do not know. Preference may grant an importance to basic sensuous satisfactions, but it runs wider, much wider, than they. They become like the relation of sense data or pointer readings to a great physical theory. You have a preference for your country as against other countries. Yet where do you get a sense experience of your country? Or a preference for the existence of something as against its non-existence, which is Brogan's definition of a good thing. But where do you get a sensuous experience of non-existence? It has to be thought. Even when you verify the better, you are comparing a present actuality with competing possibilities. The realms of the possible are not realms of either present pleasure or actual physical behavior. They are intellectual realms, wider than the actual. They have to be thought, not sensed. This is, I think, the true locus of value, as opposed to mere like and dislike. It is not a matter of mere emotion, but it is a matter of worthwhile preference. The best is what I most prefer because it has the most to offer, as a unity. Such is, to me, the significance of Brogan's theory.

We had another student in the group in 1913–14, whom none of us thought of as a genius. I spelt his name "Elliot" instead of "Eliot" in my early notes, and knew him later as Tom Eliot from St. Louis. But in course of time he was to make the name of T. S. Eliot more famous than all the rest of ours put together. His first paper was on the interpretation of primitive religions. He had been reading Durkheim, Jane Harrison, and Frazer, and wanted to know what is "interpretation" as opposed to "description"? His

year's work circled around this question of the truth of interpretations. He had been reading Francis Herbert Bradley, and said no
simple statement was absolutely true. Brogan, of course, had to
intervene to inquire if Eliot thought that last statement true? The
argument waxed hot, and finally Eliot told Brogan, "You can't
understand me. To understand my point of view, you have to believe it first." Royce intervened to say that a simple statement
might be definitely true or false, except for the fact that we can
never make a simple statement.

About all this, as James once said, "What has concluded, that
we should conclude about it?" [70] The period was one in which two
sets of sworn blood brothers, the New and the Critical Realists, met
and vowed they would coöperate. And then, like ships that pass in
the night, each went in his separate way into his separate region
of outer darkness. Philosophical coöperation we got, if ever, in a
Seminar like Royce's, the clash of opposites under the guidance of
a shrewd master who was the first among equals. When we who
were trained in such a school went riding into the visiting professor that spring, Professor Demos tells me that we horrified the
younger students, that Bertrand Arthur William Russell should
be treated just like an ordinary man. But Royce and Russell were
big enough to take it and like it. Most of us today, as philosophers,
hedge and equivocate lest we be caught off base. We do not want
to expose our half-formed thoughts to possible refutation. We are
too self-consciously proud to love the truth. "Who is the true
philosopher?" says Plato. "He who loves to look upon the truth."
I said to Professor William P. Montague, on one occasion, "Why
don't you run a seminar? You are full of ideas." He said, "I prefer
to make my mistakes in private. I can't think under public scru-
tiny." Yet Montague's great weakness was a lack of self-criticism.
He needed to come bang up against criticism. It would have stimu-
lated him to novelties he never realized. Plato said you cannot
really learn philosophy out of books; they do not explain or an-

[70] The question is slightly misquoted from Benjamin Blood.

swer back. They need the personal touch, and that was what Royce gave us.

The presence here of Professors Kallen and Loewenberg reminds me of an anecdote of those old days. Kallen once brightened up a lecture with a reference to "the whole history of philosophy, from its rise in Thales to its fall in Royce." Loewenberg came bristling back, "That young man mistakes eccentricity for originality. He has a brilliant future behind him." As I look to those times, Royce seems so real to me still, that it is hard for me to think of Royce as born a hundred years ago today.

&❧ APPENDIX B

Principal Writings of Harry Todd Costello

I BOOKS

A List of Books for a College Student's Reading. Hartford, 1925 (*Trinity College Bulletin*, N. S. Vol. XXII, No. 2). Second edition, 1928. Third edition, 1940. Fourth edition, rewritten, 1951. Fifth edition, 1958. The third and later editions are entitled *Books for a College Student's Reading.*

A Philosophy of the Real and the Possible. New York, 1954. The text of the 1952 Woodbridge Lectures, with "The Naturalism of Frederick Woodbridge."

II ESSAYS

"External Relations and the 'Argument from Missouri,' " *Journal of Philosophy*, VIII (September 14, 1911), 505–10.

"A Neo-Realistic Theory of Analysis," *Journal of Philosophy*, X (August 28, 1913), 494–98.

"Hypotheses and Instrumental Logicians," *Journal of Philosophy*, XV (January 31, 1918), 57–64.

"Old Problems with New Faces in Recent Logic," *Studies in the History of Ideas*, ed. by the Department of Philosophy of Columbia University, I, 249–67. New York, 1918.

"The Value of False Philosophies," *Journal of Philosophy*, XVI (May 22, 1919), 281–90.

"Relations between Relations," *Journal of Philosophy*, XVI (October 9, 1919), 568–74.

"Professor Dewey's 'Judgments of Practise,' " *Journal of Philosophy*, XVII (August 12, 1920), 449–55.

"A Philosopher among the Metaphysicians," *American Philosophy Today and Tomorrow*, ed. Horace M. Kallen and Sidney Hook, pp. 101–14. New York, 1935.

"The Naturalism of Frederick Woodbridge," *Naturalism and the Human Spirit*, ed. Yervant H. Krikorian, pp. 295–318. New York, 1944. Reprinted in *A Philosophy of the Real and the Possible*, pp. 124–53.

"Logic and Reality," *Journal of Philosophy*, XLIII (March 28, 1946), 169–90. A critical discussion of *A Preface to Logic*, by M. R. Cohen.

"Radical Empiricism and the Concept of 'Experienced As,' " *Journal of Philosophy*, XLV (April 22, 1948), 225–48.

"Recollections of Royce's Seminar on Comparative Methodology," *Journal of Philosophy*, LIII (February 2, 1956), 72–77. Reprinted above, pp. 189–95.

"Royce's Encyclopedia Articles," *Journal of Philosophy*, LIII (April 26, 1956), 311–13.

"Introduction to 'Notes on Logic, September, 1913,' by Ludwig Wittgenstein," *Journal of Philosophy*, LIV (April 25, 1957), 230–31.

"Logic in 1914 and Now," *Journal of Philosophy*, LIV (April 25, 1957), 245–64.

III REVIEWS IN THE *Journal of Philosophy*

D. C. Macintosh, *The Problem of Knowledge*. XIII (June 8, 1916), 309–18.

A. C. Seward, ed., *Science and the Nation*. XV (May 23, 1918), 304–06.

A. C. Crehore, *The Mystery of Matter and Energy*. XV (July 4, 1918), 389–90.

Proceedings of the Aristotelian Society, 1916–1917. XV (September 12, 1918), 529–31.

Proceedings of the Aristotelian Society, 1917–1918. XVI (July 31, 1919), 439–47.

John Mills, *The Realities of Modern Science*. XVI (November 20, 1919), 668–70.

Proceedings of the Aristotelian Society, 1918–1919. XVII (March 11, 1920), 159–65.

A. N. Whitehead, *An Enquiry Concerning the Principles of Natural Knowledge*. XVII (June 3, 1920), 326–34.

Bernard Bosanquet, *Implication and Linear Inference*. XVIII (July 21, 1921), 403–17.

F. W. Westaway, *Scientific Method: Its Philosophy and Practice*. XVIII (August 18, 1921), 472–75.

Proceedings of the Aristotelian Society, 1919–1920. XVIII (November 24, 1921), 668–70.

Proceedings of the Aristotelian Society, 1920–1921. XIX (July 20, 1922), 414–18.

C. J. Keyser, *Mathematical Philosophy: A Study of Fate and Freedom*. XX (March 1, 1923), 137–39.

J. M. Keynes, *A Treatise on Probability*. XX (May 24, 1923), 301–06.

Proceedings of the Aristotelian Society, 1921–1922. XX (October 25, 1923), 613–14.

Proceedings of the Aristotelian Society, 1922–1923; and *Relativity, Logic, and Mysticism* (Aristotelian Society Supplementary Volume III). XXI (August 14, 1924), 463–66.

Proceedings of the Aristotelian Society, 1923–1924; and *Concepts of Continuity* (Aristotelian Society Supplementary Volume IV). XXII (March 12, 1925), 163–65.

Émile Meyerson, *Identité et réalité; De l'Explication dans les sciences;* and *La Déduction relativiste.* XXII (November 5, 1925), 637–43.

E. A. Burtt, *The Metaphysical Foundations of Modern Science.* XXIII (January 21, 1926), 47–50.

Proceedings of the Aristotelian Society, 1924–1925. XXIII (April 29, 1926), 245–48.

Proceedings of the Aristotelian Society, 1925–1926; and *Methods of Analysis* (Aristotelian Society Supplementary Volume VI). XXIV (March 17, 1927), 165–66.

Proceedings of the Aristotelian Society, 1926–1927. XXV (May 10, 1928), 270–73.

A. N. Whitehead and Bertrand Russell, *Principia Mathematica,* second edition. XXV (August 2, 1928), 438–45.

Proceedings of the Aristotelian Society, 1927–1928. XXVI (April 25, 1929), 246–50.

Proceedings of the Aristotelian Society, 1928–1929. XXVII (October 23, 1930), 613–14.

G. P. Adams and W. P. Montague, eds., *Contemporary American Philosophy: Personal Statements.* XXVIII (April 23, 1931), 244–49.

Proceedings of the Aristotelian Society, 1929–1930. XXVIII (December 17, 1931), 719–20.

Proceedings of the Aristotelian Society, 1930–1931. XXIX (July 21, 1932), 419.

Ernest Nagel, *On the Logic of Measurement.* XXIX (August 18, 1932), 469–73.

Proceedings of the Aristotelian Society, 1931–1932. XXX (August 3, 1933), 444–47.

Joseph Geyser, *Das Gesetz der Ursache.* XXXI (January 4, 1934), 26–27.

Willy Moog, *Das Leben der Philosophen.* XXXI (January 18, 1934), 45–46.

Hermann Burg, *Gedanken zur Naturlehre.* XXXI (January 18, 1934), 51.

G. P. Conger, *The Horizons of Thought.* XXXI (February 1, 1934), 77–78.

Gustav Wolff, *Leben und Erkennen.* XXXI (March 1, 1934), 133.

M. R. Cohen and Ernest Nagel, *An Introduction to Logic and Scientific Method.* XXXI (April 12, 1934), 215–17.

Proceedings of the Aristotelian Society, 1932–1933; and *Creativity, Politics, and the A Priori* (Aristotelian Society Supplementary Volume XII). XXXI (April 26, 1934), 247.

C. F. Harrold, *Carlyle and German Thought.* XXXI (June 21, 1934), 361–62.

Julien Pacotte, *La Connaissance.* XXXI (July 5, 1934), 389.

W. F. G. Swann, *The Architecture of the Universe.* XXXI (September 13, 1934), 530–31.

Copernicus, *Des Révolutions des orbes célestes,* trans. A. Koyré. XXXI (October 11, 1934), 579.

Modern Tendencies in Philosophy (Aristotelian Society Supplementary Volume XIII). XXXI (October 25, 1934), 612.

Ch. Perelman, *De l'Arbitraire dans la connaissance.* XXXI (October 25, 1934), 613.

H. P. Macmillan, *Two Ways of Thinking.* XXXI (November 22, 1934), 668.

Abel Rey and others, *Science et Loi.* XXXI (December 6, 1934), 698.

Haym Jaffe, *Natural Law as Controlled But Not Determined by Experiment.* XXXII (January 3, 1935), 25.

Proceedings of the Aristotelian Society, 1933–1934. XXXII (January 31, 1935), 78.

E. T. Bell, *The Search for Truth.* XXXII (February 28, 1935), 134–35.

A. J. Hopkins, *Alchemy, Child of Greek Philosophy.* XXXII (March 14, 1935), 160–61.

Studies in the History of Ideas, Vol. III. XXII (March 14, 1935), 161–62.

II. F. Mins, Jr., *Materialism, the Scientific Bias.* XXXII (April 11, 1935), 222–23.

D. E. Richmond, *The Dilemma of Modern Physics: Waves or Particles?* XXXII (June 6, 1935), 335.

Erwin Schrödinger, *Science and the Human Temperament.* XXXII (August 1, 1935), 442–43.

Livingston Welch, *Imagination and Human Nature.* XXXII (September 12, 1935), 529.

Heinrich Schaller, *Die Renaissance.* XXXII (November 21, 1935), 666–67.

Science, History, and Theology (Aristotelian Society Supplementary Volume XIV). XXXII (December 5, 1935), 693–94.

Proceedings of the Aristotelian Society, 1934–1935. XXXII (December 19, 1935), 719.

G. C. Field, *Studies in Philosophy.* XXXIII (February 27, 1936), 136–37.

G. T. W. Patrick, *Introduction to Philosophy.* XXXIII (March 12, 1936), 160–61.

Julius Schultz, *Das Ich und die Physik.* XXXIII (March 12, 1936), 166.

A. O. Lovejoy and George Boas, *Primitivism and Related Ideas in Antiquity.* XXXIII (March 26, 1936), 192–93.

Urpo Harva, *Die Philosophie von G. I. Hartman.* XXXIII (April 9, 1936), 222–23.

E. A. Moody, *The Logic of William of Ockham.* XXXIII (April 23, 1936), 247–48.

H. H. Price, *Truth and Corrigibility.* XXXIII (September 10, 1936), 526–27.

Ernst Zimmer, *The Revolution in Physics.* XXXIII (September 10, 1936), 527–28.

A. O. Lovejoy, *The Great Chain of Being.* XXXIII (October 8, 1936), 580–81.

What Can Philosophy Determine? (Aristotelian Society Supplementary Volume XV). XXXIII (November 19, 1936), 668–69.

J.-J. Vallory, *Poussières de physique,* Vol. I. XXXIII (December 3, 1936), 697.

L. R. Heath, *The Concept of Time.* XXXIV (March 18, 1937), 164–65.

E. W. Strong, *Procedures and Metaphysics: A Study in the Philosophy of Mathematical-Physical Science in the Sixteenth and Seventeenth Centuries.* XXXIV (June 10, 1937), 329.

Albert Eagle, *The Philosophy of Religion versus the Philosophy of Science.* XXXIV (June 24, 1937), 363.

C. J. Eustace, *Mind and the Mystery.* XXXIV (September 16, 1937), 529–30.

Joseph Needham, *Integrative Levels: A Revaluation of the Idea of Progress.* XXXIV (October 28, 1937), 612–13.

M. J. Adler, *What Man Has Made of Man.* XXXIV (November 25, 1937), 670–71.

W. R. Thompson, *Science and Common Sense: An Aristotelian Excursion.* XXXIV (December 23, 1937), 720.

M. M. Black, *The Pendulum Swings Back.* XXXV (March 3, 1938), 138.

Proceedings of the Aristotelian Society, 1936–1937; and *Knowledge and Fore-knowledge* (Aristotelian Society Supplementary Volume XVI). XXXV (April 14, 1938), 217–18.

Alwin Mittasch, *Katalyse und Determinismus: Ein Beitrag zur Philosophie der Chemie.* XXXV (April 14, 1938), 221–22.

La Notion de progrès devant la science actuelle (Sixième Semaine Internationale de Synthèse). XXXV (May 12, 1938), 278–79.

Rasvihary Das, *The Philosophy of Whitehead.* XXXV (September 1, 1938), 493–94.

K. W. Wild, *Intuition.* XXXV (September 1, 1938), 495–96.

J. W. Dunne, *The Serial Universe.* XXXV (October 13, 1938), 584–85.

R. B. Levinson, ed., *The College Journey: An Introduction to the Fields of College Study.* XXXV (November 10, 1938), 642.

T. M. Greene, ed., *The Meaning of the Humanities: Five Essays.* XXXVI (January 19, 1939), 52–53.

Ernest Nagel, *Principles of the Theory of Probability*. XXXVI (March 16, 1939), 163–65.

Proceedings of the Aristotelian Society, 1937–1938; and *Action, Perception, and Measurement* (Aristotelian Society Supplementary Volume XVII). XXXVI (April 13, 1939), 216–17.

C. C. Pratt, *The Logic of Modern Psychology*. XXXVI (August 3, 1939), 447.

Antonio Giao, *Phénoménologie unitaire: recherches sur les propriétés générales de l'évolution*. XXXVI (September 14, 1939), 531.

Proceedings of the Aristotelian Society, 1938–1939; and *Hume and Present Day Problems* (Aristotelian Society Supplementary Volume XVIII). XXXVII (February 1, 1940), 75–77.

C. M. Perry, *The Multidimensional Society: Directions in the Midst of Change*. XXXVII (June 6, 1940), 334–35.

J. J. Rolbiecki, *The Prospects of Philosophy*. XXXVII (August 29, 1940), 502.

W. J. Norton, Jr., *Bishop Butler: Moralist and Divine*. XXXVIII (January 16, 1941), 50–51.

J. H. Randall, Jr., *The Making of the Modern Mind*. XXXVIII (February 13, 1941), 108–09.

Sir Charles Sherrington, *Man on His Nature*. XXXVIII (June 19, 1941), 359–62.

A. P. Ushenko, *The Problems of Logic*. XXXVIII (July 3, 1941), 381–84.

Armand Lowinger, *The Methodology of Pierre Duhem*. XXXIX (March 12, 1942), 160–63.

A. J. Krzesinski, *Is Modern Culture Doomed?* XXXIX (May 7, 1942), 278.

Benjamin Brickman, *An Introduction to Francesco Patrizi's Nova de Universis Philosophia*. XL (March 4, 1943), 136.

Rudolf Jordan, *We Are Ancestors, or The Age of Responsibility*. XL (November 25, 1943), 670–71.

Norman Foerster, ed., *The Humanities after the War: The Baconian Lectures, 1943*. XLI (July 20, 1944), 416–17.

C. E. Raven, *Science, Religion, and the Future*. XLII (March 15, 1945), 166–67.

José Ortega y Gasset, *Mission of the University*. XLII (June 7, 1945), 332–33.

Sir Richard Clifford Tute, *After Materialism—What?* XLII (July 19, 1945), 418–20.

R. S. Lillie, *General Biology and Philosophy of Organism*. XLIII (August 15, 1946), 475–76.

R. C. Lodge, *Philosophy of Business*. XLIII (August 29, 1946), 503.

Analysis and Metaphysics (Aristotelian Society Supplementary Volume XIX). XLIV (April 10, 1947), 216–18.

H. M. Bhattacharyya, *The Principles of Philosophy*. XLIV (April 24, 1947), 247.

Irwin Edman, *Philosopher's Quest.* XLIV (August 14, 1947), 476.

R. B. Heywood, ed., *The Works of the Mind.* XLV (February 12, 1948), 108–09.

C. E. M. Joad, *How Our Minds Work;* and Peter Fireman, *Sound Thinking.* XLV (February 12, 1948), 109.

F. S. C. Northrop, *The Logic of the Sciences and the Humanities.* XLVI (March 17, 1949), 158–60.

A. W. Brown, *The Metaphysical Society: Victorian Minds in Crisis, 1869–1880.* XLVI (May 26, 1949), 364.

M. R. Cohen, *Studies in Philosophy and Science.* XLVI (October 13, 1949), 678–79.

Logic and Reality (Aristotelian Society Supplementary Volume XX); *Explanation in History and Philosophy* (*id.*, XXI); and *Logical Positivism and Ethics* (*id.*, XXII). XLVI (October 27, 1949), 708–11.

A. O. Lovejoy, *Essays in the History of Ideas.* XLVII (January 5, 1950), 22–23.

H. H. Price, *Harold Arthur Prichard, 1871–1947.* XLVII (April 27, 1950), 274–75.

R. C. Stauffer, ed., *Science and Civilization.* XLVII (June 8, 1950), 366–67.

F. J. Teggart, ed., *The Idea of Progress: A Collection of Readings.* XLVII (July 6, 1950), 420–21.

Dante, *La Divina Commedia: Inferno,* trans. H. M. Ayres; and *On World-Government, or De Monarchia,* trans. H. W. Schneider. XLVII (August 3, 1950), 473.

Harold Selsam, ed., *Handbook of Philosophy.* XLVII (August 17, 1950), 505.

Helge Lundholm, *God's Failure or Man's Folly.* XLVII (August 17, 1950), 505–06.

Nicholas Pastore, *The Nature-Nurture Controversy.* XLVII (August 17, 1950), 506.

Proceedings of the Aristotelian Society, 1939–1940; id., 1940–1941; *id.,* 1941–1942; *id.,* 1942–1943; *id.,* 1943–1944; *id.,* 1944–1945. XLVII (August 31, 1950), 532–33.

R. M. Hutchins, *Saint Thomas and the World State.* XLVII (August 31, 1950), 535–36.

Max Black, *Language and Philosophy: Studies in Method.* XLVII (October 12, 1950), 608–10.

Philipp Frank, *Modern Science and Its Philosophy;* and *Relativity: A Richer Truth.* XLVII (November 9, 1950), 666–71.

S. P. Lamprecht, *Nature and History.* XLVIII (March 1, 1951), 151–53.

Theodore Brameld, *Ends and Means in Education: A Midcentury Appraisal.* XLVIII (April 26, 1951), 312–13.

Sidney Greenberg, *The Infinite in Giordano Bruno, with a Translation of His*

Dialogue, Concerning the Cause, Principle, and One. XLVIII (May 24, 1951), 368–69.

Ernest Nagel, ed., *John Stuart Mill's Philosophy and Scientific Method.* XLVIII (June 7, 1951), 395–96.

Albert Einstein, *Out of My Later Years;* and P. W. Bridgman, *Reflections of a Physicist.* XLVIII (June 21, 1951), 427.

Werner Heisenberg, *Philosophic Problems of Nuclear Science.* L (March 12, 1953), 196–97.

IV OTHER PUBLICATIONS

[Review of] R. M. Eaton, *Symbolism and Truth, Philosophical Review,* XXXV (November, 1926), 574.

[Review of] E. L. Schaub, ed., *Philosophy To-day, Philosophical Review,* XXXVIII (July, 1929), 395–98.

"Letter to the Editors," *Journal of Philosophy,* XXXI (May 24, 1934), 307–08.

[Review of] M. J. Adler, *Saint Thomas and the Gentiles, Ethics,* XLIX (April, 1939), 373–74.

✌ INDEX OF PROPER NAMES